As in the notable companion volume to this work, DRAGONS, ELVES, AND HEROES, these are tales of fantasy, of wonder, myth, glory—heroic chronicles in the tradition of the ancient legends. These are the tales by contemporary writers that prove magic has not left the world, that mysterious powers and epic deeds still hold the fascination for mankind that they did when stories were told by word-of-mouth. So the young magicians of the title carry on the tradition in tales that charm, terrify, enchant, embolden and reassure.

For if it is true that the reading world is turning more and more to fantasy to escape the awesome realities of our world, it is equally true that man models himself on that larger-than-life figure, that God, or gods, that heroic knight or seductive enchantress, that being with the extra power to dare what mere mortals cannot—but whose courage is very mortal indeed. And always there is the reinforcing knowledge that it is men who weave these tales . . .

So here are magnificent works by Morris, Eddison, Cabell, Merritt, Dunsany, Lovecraft, Smith, Carter, Howard, de Camp, Kuttner, Vance, Lewis and finally, new poems by that magician without whom no anthology of contemporary fantasy would be complete—J. R. R. Tolkien.

Other Lin Carter titles

TOLKIEN: A LOOK BEHIND
THE LORD OF THE RINGS
DRAGONS, ELVES, AND HEROES (Ed.)

Also available from Ballantine Books.

This is an original publication—not a reprint.

The Young Magicians

Edited,
with an Introduction
and Notes
by
Lin Carter

BALLANTINE BOOKS • NEW YORK

THE MAZE OF MAAL DWEB, by Clark Ashton Smith, originally published as "The Maze of The Enchanter" in *The Double Shadow and Other Fantasies* (Auburn, Cal.: Privately Published, 1933) and copyright 1933 by Clark Ashton Smith; also appeared in *Weird Tales* for October, 1938, copyright 1938 by the Popular Fiction Publishing Company; and in *Lost Worlds* (Sauk City, Wis.: Arkham House, 1944), copyright 1944 by Clark Ashton Smith. Reprinted by permission of Arkham House.

THROUGH THE DRAGON GLASS, by A. Merritt, which originally appeared in *All Story Weekly* for November 24, 1917, is from *The Fox Woman & Other Stories* (New York: Avon Publishing Company, Inc., 1949), copyright 1917, 1945 by Eleanor H. Merritt. Reprinted by permission of Brandt & Brandt.

THE VALLEY OF THE WORM, by Robert E. Howard, which originally appeared in *Weird Tales* for February, 1934, copyright 1934 by the Popular Fiction Publishing Company, is from *Skull-Face and Others* (Sauk City, Wis.: Arkham House, 1946), copyright 1946 by August Derleth. Reprinted by permission of Glenn Lord, agent for the estate of Robert E. Howard.

HELDENDAMMERUNG, by L. Sprague de Camp, originally appeared in *Amra*, vol. 2, no. 29; copyright © 1964 by L. Sprague de Camp. Reprinted by permission of L. Sprague de Camp.

CURSED BE THE CITY, by Henry Kuttner, which originally appeared in *Strange Stories* for April, 1939, copyright © 1939, 1966 by Henry Kuttner, is reprinted by permission of the Harold Matson Co., Inc.

KA THE APPALLING, by L. Sprague de Camp, was originally published in *Fantastic Universe Science Fiction* for August, 1958; copyright © 1958 by King-Size Publications, Inc. Reprinted by permission of L. Sprague de Camp.

TURJAN OF MIIR, by Jack Vance, was originally published in *The Dying Earth* (New York: Hillman Periodicals, 1950); copyright © 1950 by Jack Vance; reprinted with the permission of the author and his agents, Scott Meredith Literary Agency, Inc., 580 Fifth Avenue, New York, New York, 10036.

NARNIAN SUITE, by C. S. Lewis, which originally appeared in *Punch* for November 4, 1953, is from *Poems* by C. S. Lewis (New York: Harcourt, Brace & World, Inc., 1965), edited by Walter Hooper, copyright © 1964 by The Executor of the Estate of C. S. Lewis. Reprinted by permission of Harcourt, Brace & World, Inc.

ONCE UPON A TIME, by J.R.R. Tolkien, copyright © 1965 by the Macmillan Company; reprinted by permission of J.R.R. Tolkien.

THE DRAGON'S VISIT, by J.R.R. Tolkien, copyright © 1965 by the Macmillan Company; reprinted by permission of J.R.R. Tolkien.

First Printing: October, 1969

Printed in the United States of America

BALLANTINE BOOKS, INC.
101 Fifth Avenue, New York, New York 10003

Cover Painting: Sheryl Slavitt

THE YOUNG MAGICIANS
is dedicated to
the man who invented fantasy,
WILLIAM MORRIS
and to those living writers,
his spiritual descendents, who,
for one or another reason, are not
represented herein:
Lloyd Alexander
Poul Anderson
Jane Gaskell
John Jakes
Fritz Leiber
Michael Moorcock,
AND
Andre Norton.

Contents

Introduction

Diana's Foresters

By "TOLKIENIAN" FANTASY, I mean stories of warfare, quest or adventure set in imaginary worlds or lands or ages of the author's own invention: worlds where magic really works and the gods are real. Which means: stories more or less similar in style, mood and setting to J. R. R. Tolkien's magnificent fantasy epic *The Lord of the Rings*.

Tolkien's book is a masterprice of disciplined imagination, and the greatest wonder-tale of our time, but it is far from being unique. There are many such stories, and at one time they were very widely popular. Today, reading tastes have turned more to the story of social or psychological realism set in modern scenery, and this change has pushed the wonder-tale aside, relegating many of our finest traditional adult fantasies to the dustier and less-frequented back shelves of your public library.

But such tales have always been with us. They go back to the very dawn of literature itself. The earliest stories known are adventure fantasies laid in more-or-less imaginary settings, as a glance at the *Odyssey* or the *Gilgamesh Epic* or the pages of Herodotus and Pliny will prove. Man has always loved tales of marvel and mystery in the glamorous scenery of curious, far-off lands—not so much because he is a credulous animal (although he is that), but simply because it is part of the nature of man to have an appetite for Marvels.

It is strange, and more than a trifle sad, that some people simply cannot understand or sympathize with our taste for such tales. Respected literary critics and distinguished novelists and otherwise intelligent educators tend to look askance at such reading-matter. The man who lives next door—perhaps even your wife—is amused and more than a little contemptuous to find you reading such a book as this one. To them it seems childish for a grown man of intelligence and intellectual curiosity to want to read about dragons, knights, witches and magic rings. They call such stories "fairy-tales"—as if the term of itself carried a derogatory connotation!—and seem to be infuriated that an adult could waste his time with such stuff. After all, they argue, everyone *knows* dragons are not real, there are no knights or witches these days and magic rings do not work.

It is almost impossible to argue with such a point of view. People who do not themselves read or enjoy fantasy have no conception of *why* we read it or of the kind of enjoyment we derive from it. But the next time you suffer the indignity of such a put-down, you might try defending your reading taste with this line of reasoning:

We read fantasy not so much to *escape* from life (that is one of their labels, "escapist reading"), but to *enlarge* our spectrum of life-experience, to enrich it and to extend the range of our experience into regions we can never visit in the flesh. For fantasy is not all airy-fairy nonsense, it can be deadly serious and deeply meaningful. Of course it is true that dragons do not exist (alas!): but the Dragon is not just a king-sized crocodile to us—it is a hieroglyph of the imagination, and it symbolizes the terror and beauty and awe of that side of nature we call The Destroyer. And of course there are no more real witches—there probably never were, at least not the bent, malefic crones of the Brothers Grimm—but Evil is real enough, and all too common, and we learn and savor something of its nature through the figure of the

Witch. And perhaps there are no more real knights, no
pure and noble heroes of selflessness and strength. But
heroism and nobility and unselfish courage do exist, and
it is good to be reminded of the fact through so glittering and romantic a symbol. And as for magic talismans,
I thank whatever gods may be that the world is still rich
in Magic. I own such a talisman myself. It is a little ce-
ramic figure of a dog the size of your thumb-nail. It is
only a dime-store jimcrack, but I would not sell it for a
hundred times its value. I picked it up in my backyard
when I was about five years old: I found it on the afternoon I came running home, filled with the thrilling news
that on that day I had learned how to spell *cat* and *dog*.
To me, that worthless little figure is a magic key. I as-
sociate it with the opening-up of the most enchanted
world I know—the world of books. For me, the chipped
little china dog is embued with glowing and wondrous
associations. And that *is* Magic!

So in the reading of fantasy we deepen and enrich our
life-experience. For we are dealing, not with imaginary
things which do not exist, but with gigantic and eternal
realities which are among the deepest and most meaningful things in life. Professor Tolkien has said all of this
much more concisely and beautifully that I can say it, so
let me quote from his famous essay "On Fairy-Stories":

> *By the forging of Gram cold iron was revealed; by the mak-
> ing of Pegasus horses were ennobled; in the Trees of the Sun
> and Moon root and stock, flower and fruit are manifested in
> glory.*

Beyond the fact that fantasy deals meaningfully with the
great archetypes of human experience, there is also the
lure and luster of the far-off, the remote, the little-
known. Possibly the most magical and evocative phrase
in the English language is

> *Over the hills and far away,*

and this is not merely my own opinion, but the judge-
ment of literature. The mere speaking-aloud of those six

words sets a person dreaming: if it were not so, it would not have been used by poet after poet after poet. No one knows the forgotten genius who first coined this haunting phrase, but you will find it in the nursery-rhyme "Tom, Tom, the Piper's Son." And in the works of the 17th Century poet Thomas D'Urfey; and in *The Beggar's Opera;* and in a poem of Chesterton; and a poem called "The Hills of Ruel" by Fiona Macleod; and even (for that matter) in one of my own verses.

Man has always delighted in things fabulous and far-away. From the beginning, man saw himself as *Homo viator,* Man the Voyager, and the most familiar symbol for man's life is that of the Journey: the adventure through a world filled with shadowy perils and wonders, on the road that stretches between those twin portals of the Unknown we call Birth and Death.

The temptation to stray from that path whereon we all tread, to turn aside for a time, to go at right angles to Reality, as it were, has proved irresistible to a very large number of the world's authors.

Early writers did not find it necessary to invent imaginary worlds, because the world itself was still largely unknown, unexplored, unmapped. The forgotten storytellers of Grimm's *Märchen* did not have to go far afield to find a fitting home for their ogres and witches and enchanted princesses: the forest that lay, thick and dark and mysterious, just beyond the next farm would do. Homer, who sang for a sea-going people, did not have to venture outside the world to the Circumambient Main, the world-encircling Ocean River, for his fabulous locales: only a few days journey by sea from Troy was far enough away to be the location of Circe's isle of Aeaea or Calypso's Ogygia, or the country of the Cyclops. Chrétien and the other Arthurian romancers were mostly Frenchmen writing about an ancient and mythological Britain, so there was no need to create a new geography for Camelot the City of Marvel.

But by the 17th and 18th Centuries, it was beginning to get difficult to write wonder-tales because we knew much more about the real world, and were finding out more all the time. Voltaire had to go to America for a site remote enough from everyday experience to serve as the locale of *Candide*'s El Dorado. And the fabulous Kingdom of Prester John got shoved off the map frequently. First it was supposed to be in India; then, when we got to know quite a bit about India, tale-tellers located it on the shadowy borders of Cathay; finally it ended up in the depths of Africa.

And by the 19th Century, things really got tough for the tellers of fantastic tales. That is why such stories from that period seem dated when we read them today. Even the best of them: it is hard, even when reading so splendid a romance as H. Rider Haggard's *She* or *King Solomon's Mines*, to retain the suspension of disbelief necessary to the enjoyment of such tales, because we know that the site of the Lost City of Kôr is now the scene of a Mau Mau uprising, and that the country where Allan Quatermain discovered Solomon's lost diamond mines is now bidding for membership in the United Nations.

The authors of the wonder-tale solved this problem in three ways. They turned to the remote past and wrote stories laid in the Lost Continent of Atlantis. Or they invented science fiction and found a fertile field for Marvels on the dead sea-bottoms of Mars or the mysterious caverns within the Moon, or on a planet circling a remote star. Or they invented the purely imaginary world for their settings. And, in so doing, laid the foundations of the tradition whereof *The Lord of the Rings* is but the most recent, and probably the finest, example.

*

The first writer to do this with any particular degree of success in recent fiction was William Morris. His misty, Medieval worldscapes were swiftly followed by Lord Dunsany's little kingdoms "at the edge of the world" or, at least, "beyond the Lands We Know." And by other experiments in neogeography from the hands of such writers as Eddison, Cabell, Lovecraft, Clark Ashton Smith and Robert E. Howard, and many more—most of whom are represented herein.

Of course, many writers toyed with the pleasures of world-making before William Morris arrived on the scene, and we need not go all the way back to Homer and the *Gilgamesh*-poet to find them. When Plato soberly recorded the history of Atlantis and placed it in the shadowy seas beyond the Pillars of Hercules, he was world-making. So was Scheherezade (that most gifted story-teller of them all), when she dispatched Sindbad to the isle of Kasil, the Valley of Diamonds, or the country where the Roc builds its colossal nest.

But the history of literature is a complex overlapping pattern at best. There were lost cities in literature before *She*, tales of terror before *The Castle of Otranto*, and stories of mystery and detection before Poe*—but we measure the beginnings of a new literary tradition, usually, from the author who really makes an impact with his innovation, and who starts a trend. Hence we consider that the heroic fantasy laid in an imaginary world really begins with *The Wood Beyond the World* by William Morris, which was first published on May 11, 1895.

This anthology is devoted to those fantasy writers in this genre who derive from the Morris tradition. A companion volume entitled *Dragons, Elves, and Heroes* (published by Ballantine Books simultaneously with this book) presents the best examples I can find of the same sort of thing, but done by writers who lived before Morris. In the main, this companion anthology draws from ancient epic and saga literature—*Beowulf*, the *Kalevala*, the *Volsunga Saga*—or from mythological texts such as the Welsh *Mabinogion*, the Persian *Shah Namah*, or the Icelandic *Elder Edda*. A reading of both anthologies will, I hope, give you a good understanding of just what has been done in this field of the imaginary-world fantasy up to our time.

Each selection is prefaced with a brief note on the au-

* *Hamlet* is a murder-mystery, for instance. So is *Oedipus Rex*, for that matter.

thor's life and work, and for the convenience of interested novices who have little familiarity with this kind of story, I have appended a selected bibliography of other books by the writers herein included or referred to: for the sake of convenience, I have listed only those titles currently available in paperback.

It is heartening to realize that not all of these writers belong to the dead past. Of the fourteen authors represented here, four are still alive and still working in the genre. And, while for one or another reason I have not been able to include a specimen of their work in this anthology, there are many other writers now working in the Morris/Dunsany/Eddison/Tolkien tradition: writers like Fritz Leiber, Poul Anderson and John Jakes here in America, and British authors such as Jane Gaskell and Michael Moorcock, whose recent contributions to the genre have been intelligent, imaginative and important.

Those of us who write this kind of fantasy are still few: but our numbers increase. Nor need we, I think, be ashamed of our calling. Shakespeare had something to say on this; it is relevant to our art, although he really meant it to be applied in another context. Do you recall Falstaff's words in the First Part of *King Henry IV*, Act I, Scene 2—?

Let not us that are squires of the night's body be called thieves of the day's beauty; let us be Diana's foresters, gentlemen of the shade, minions of the moon. . . .

Even in this dreary age, Diana still hath a few foresters who strive to preserve and to continue an ancient, magical and shadowy art. I give you here a bookfull of our tales.

And there are many more to come.

LIN CARTER
Editorial Consultant
The Ballantine Adult Fantasy Series

Hollis, Long Island, New York

Rapunzel

❖━━━━━━━━━━━━━━━━━❖

WILLIAM MORRIS (1834–96) was the first English writer
of any consequence to explore the possibilities of the fantastic tale of wanderings, and adventure laid in completely imaginary surroundings. He was the first to write
novels of warfare and quest laid in invented, pseudo-Medieval worldscapes where magic works: and, as such, he
laid the foundations for the epic fantasy tradition carried
on after his death by Lord Dunsany, E. R. Eddison, C.
S. Lewis, Fletcher Pratt, L. Sprague de Camp, James
Branch Cabell, Robert E. Howard, J. R. R. Tolkien and
others—most of whom are represented herein. As the original founder of this fantasy tradition, it is most fitting
that our collection begins with a little-known selection
from William Morris.

To put it bluntly, Morris was an eccentric in the grand
old British tradition, and a particularly fascinating one.
In revolt against the squalor and industrialization of his
century, he turned to a romantic vision of the Middle
Ages and idealized this period to the point of utopianism.
Leagued with kindred souls, like the famous pre-Ra-
phaelite painter Sir Edward Burne-Jones, whom he had
known from their undergraduate days together at Oxford, he launched a full-scale crusade to restore the tradi-
tions of Medieval arts and crafts. From his "factory" soon
poured a flood of pseudo-Medieval Morris-designed art-
works to deluge the bewildered Victorians: stained-glass

windows, tapestries, wallpaper, architectural designs, paintings, furniture, carpets, books and even illuminated manuscripts.

Among other things, he was a political thinker of considerable importance (a pioneer socialist, he helped form the Socialist League in 1884 and edited *Commonweal* until 1890), a very gifted poet (so prominent that his *Defense of Guenevere* is today considered one of the jewels of Victorian poetry; he was offered the poetry professorship of Oxford in 1877 but declined), a translator of enormous importance (his one-man "discovery" of the Scandinavian sagas helped shape the reading taste of a whole generation: among others, he produced with the help of Eiríkr Magnússon English versions of *Grettir,* the *Eyrbyggja,* the *Volsunga Saga,* etc., plus book-length poems of his own on Scandinavian subjects, a modern Jason and the Argonauts epic, and translations of *Beowulf,* the *Aeneid,* and Homer!), and—almost in passing— he was a novelist, too.

Most of his fantasy-world novels, such as *The Wood Beyond the World* (1895) and *The Well at the World's End* (1896), will be included in The Ballantine Adult Fantasy Series. So, for a Morris selection to include in *The Young Magicians* I have had to travel rather far afield to avoid duplicating material. Luckily, I uncovered this unusual tale, "Rapunzel," which might best be described as a fairy-tale retold in the form of a verse-play: to the best of my knowledge it has not been printed since about 1908 and should thus be unfamiliar to just about all my readers . . . .

———◆———

THE PRINCE, *being in the wood*
near the tower, in the evening:

I could not even think
  What made me weep that day,
When out of the council-hall
  The courtiers pass'd away,—

THE WITCH:

Rapunzel, Rapunzel,
Let down your hair!

RAPUNZEL:

It is not true that every day
She climbeth up the same strange way,
Her scarlet cloak spread broad and gay
Over my golden hair?

THE PRINCE:

And left me there alone,
   To think on what they said;
"Thou art a king's own son,
   'Tis fit that thou should'st wed."

THE WITCH:

Rapunzel, Rapunzel,
Let down your hair!

RAPUNZEL:

When I undo the knotted mass,
Fathoms below the shadows pass
Over my hair along the grass,
O my golden hair!

THE PRINCE:

I put my armour on,
   Thinking on what they said;
"Thou art a king's own son,
   'Tis fit that thou should'st wed."

THE WITCH:

Rapunzel, Rapunzel,
Let down your hair!

RAPUNZEL:

See on the marble parapet,
I lean my brow, strive to forget

That fathoms below my hair grows wet
With the dew, my golden hair.

THE PRINCE:

I rode throughout the town,
  Men did not bow the head,
Though I was the king's own son;
  "He rides to dream," they said.

THE WITCH:

Rapunzel, Rapunzel,
Wind up your hair!

RAPUNZEL:

See on the marble parapet,
The faint red stains with tears are wet;
The long years pass, no help comes yet
To free my golden hair.

THE PRINCE:

For leagues and leagues I rode,
  Till hot my armour grew,
Till underneath the leaves
  I felt the evening dew.

THE WITCH:

Rapunzel, Rapunzel,
Weep through your hair!

RAPUNZEL:

And yet—but I am growing old,
For want of love my heart is cold,
Years pass, the while I loose and fold
The fathoms of my hair.

*

THE PRINCE, *in the morning*:

I have heard tales of men, who in the night
  Saw paths of stars let down to earth from heaven,

Who follow'd them until they reach'd the light
   Wherein they dwell, whose sins are all forgiven;

But who went backward when they saw the gate
   Of diamond, nor dared to enter in;
All their life long they were content to wait,
   Purging them patiently of every sin.

I must have had a dream of some such thing,
   And now am just awakening from that dream;
For even in grey dawn those strange words ring
   Through heart and brain, and still I see that gleam.

For in my dream at sunset-time I lay
   Beneath these beeches, mail and helmet off,
Right full of joy that I had come away
   From court; for I was patient of the scoff

That met me always there from day to day,
   From any knave or coward of them all;
I was content to live that wretched way;
   For truly till I left the council-hall,

And rode forth arm'd beneath the burning sun
   My gleams of happiness were faint and few,
But then I saw my real life had begun,
   And that I should be strong quite well I knew.

For I was riding out to look for love,
   Therefore the birds within the thickets sung
Even in hot noontide, as I pass'd, above
   The elms o'ersway'd with longing towards me hung.

Now some few fathoms from the place where I
   Lay in the beechwood, was a tower fair,
The marble corners faint against the sky;
   And dreamily I wonder'd what lived there:

Because it seem'd a dwelling for a queen,
   No belfry for the swinging of great bells;

No bolt or stone had ever crushed the green
   Shafts, amber and rose walls, no soot that tells

Of the Norse torches burning up the roofs,
   On the flower-carven marble could I see;
But rather on all sides I saw the proofs
   Of a great loneliness that sicken'd me;

Making me feel a doubt that was not fear,
   Whether my whole life long had been a dream,
And I should wake up soon in some place, where
   The piled-up arms of the fighting angels gleam;

Not born as yet, but going to be born,
   No naked baby as I was at first,
But an arméd knight, whom fire, hate and scorn
   Could turn from nothing: my heart almost burst

Beneath the beeches, as I lay a-dreaming,
   I tried so hard to read this riddle through,
To catch some golden cord that I saw gleaming
   Like gossamer against the autumn blue.

But while I ponder'd these things, from the wood
   There came a black-hair'd woman, tall and bold,
Who strode straight up to where the tower stood,
   And cried out shrilly words, whereon behold—

THE WITCH, *from the tower*:

Rapunzel, Rapunzel,
Let down your hair!

THE PRINCE:

Ah Christ! it was no dream then, but there stood
   (She comes again) a maiden passing fair,
Against the roof, with face turn'd to the wood;
   Bearing within her arms waves of her yellow hair.

I read my riddle when I saw her stand,
   Poor love! Her face quite pale against her hair,

Praying to all the leagues of empty land
   To save her from the woe she suffer'd there.

To think! they trod upon her golden hair
   In the witches' sabbaths; it was a delight
For these foul things, while she, with thin feet bare,
   Stood on the roof upon the winter night,

To plait her dear hair into many plaits,
   And then, while God's eye look'd upon the thing,
In the very likenesses of Devil's bats,
   Upon the ends of her long hair to swing.

And now she stood above the parapet.
   And, spreading out her arms, let her hair flow,
Beneath that veil her smooth white forehead set
   Upon the marble, more I do not know;

Because before my eyes a film of gold
   Floated, as now it floats. O, unknown love,
Would that I could thy yellow stair behold,
   If still thou standest with lead roof above!

THE WITCH, *as she passes:*
Is there any who will dare
To climb up the yellow stair?
Glorious Rapunzel's golden hair?

THE PRINCE:
If it would please God make you sing again,
   I think that I might very sweetly die,
My soul somehow reach heaven in joyous pain,
   My heavy body on the beech-nuts lie.

Now I remember; what a most strange year,
   Most strange and awful, in the beechen wood
I have pass'd now; I still have a faint fear
   It is a kind of dream not understood.

I have seen no one in this wood except
   The witch and her; have heard no human tones,

But when the witches' revelry has crept
   Between the very jointing of my bones.

Ah! I know now; I could not go away,
   But needs must stop to hear her sing that song
She always sings at dawning of the day.
   I am not happy here, for I am strong,

And every morning do I whet my sword,
   Yet Rapunzel still weeps within the tower,
And still God ties me down to the green sward,
   Because I cannot see the gold stair floating lower.

      RAPUNZEL *sings from the tower:*
My mother taught me prayers
To say when I had need;
I have so many cares,
That I can take no heed
Of many words in them;
But I remember this:
Christ, bring me to thy bliss,
Mary, maid withouten wem,
Keep me! I am lone, I wis,
Yet besides I have made this
By myself: *Give me a kiss,*
Dear God, dwelling up in heaven!

Also: *Send me a true knight,*
Lord Christ, with a steel sword, bright
Broad, and trenchant; yeah, and seven
Spans from hilt to point, O Lord!
And let the handle of his sword
Be gold on silver, Lord in heaven!
Such a sword as I see gleam
Sometimes, when they let me dream.

Yea, besides, I have made this:
Lord, give Mary a dear kiss,
And let gold Michael, who look'd down,
When I was here, on Rouen town

From the spire, bring me that kiss
On a lily! Lord do this!

These prayers on the dreadful nights,
When the witches plait my hair,
And the fearfullest of sights
On the earth and in the air,
Will not let me close my eyes,
I murmur often, mix'd with sighs,
That my weak heart will not hold
At some things that I behold.
Nay, not sighs, but quiet groans,
That swell out the little bones
Of my bosom; till a trance
God sends in middle of that dance,
And I behold the countenance
Of Michael, and can feel no more
The bitter east wind biting sore
My naked feet; can see no more
The crayfish on the leaden floor,
That mock with feeler and grim claw.

   Yea, often in that happy trance,
Beside the blesséd countenance
Of golden Michael, on the spire
Glowing all crimson in the fire
Of sunset, I behold a face,
Which sometime, if God give me grace,
May kiss me in this very place.

*

Evening, in the tower
RAPUNZEL:
It grows half way between the dark and light;
   Love, we have been six hours here alone,
I fear that she will come before the night,
   And if she finds us thus we are undone.

THE PRINCE:

Nay, draw a little nearer, that your breath
  May touch my lips, let my cheek feel your arm;
Now tell me, did you ever see a death,
  Or ever see a man take mortal harm?

RAPUNZEL:

Once came two knights and fought with swords below,
  And while they fought I scarce could look at all,
My head swam so, after a moaning low
  Drew my eyes down; I saw against the wall

One knight lean dead, bleeding from head and breast,
  Yet seem'd it like a line of poppies red
In the golden twilight, as he took his rest,
  In the dusky time he scarcely seemed dead.

But the other, on his face six paces off,
  Lay moaning, and the old familiar name
He mutter'd through the grass, seem'd like a scoff
  Of some lost soul remembering his past fame.

His helm all dinted lay beside him there,
  The visor-bars were twisted towards the face,
The crest, which was a lady very fair,
  Wrought wonderfully was shifted from its place.

The shower'd mail-rings on the speed-walk lay,
  Perhaps my eyes were dazzled with the light
That blazed in the west, yet surely on that day
  Some crimson thing had changed the grass from bright

Pure green I love so. But the knight who died
  Lay there for days after the other went;
Until one day I heard a voice that cried,
  "Fair knight, I see Sir Robert we were sent

"To carry dead or living to the king."
  So the knights came and bore him straight away

On their lance truncheons, such a batter'd thing,
  His mother had not known him on that day,

But for his helm-crest, a gold lady fair
  Wrought wonderfully.

THE PRINCE:
          Ah, they were brothers then,
And often rode together, doubtless where
The swords were thickest, and were loyal men,
  Until they fell in these same evil dreams.

RAPUNZEL:
Yes, love, but shall we not depart from hence?
  The white moon groweth golden fast, and gleams
Between the aspen stems; I fear—and yet a sense

Of fluttering victory comes over me,
  That will not let me fear aright; my heart—
Feel how it beats, love, strives to get to thee,
  I breathe so fast that my lips needs must part;
Your breath swims round my mouth, but let us go.

THE PRINCE:
  I, Sebald, also, pluck from off the staff
The crimson banner, let it lie below,
  Above it in the wind let grasses laugh.

Now let us go, love, down the winding stair,
  With fingers intertwined: ay, feel my sword!
I wrought it long ago, with golden hair
  Flowing about the hilts, because a word,

Sung by a minstrel old, had set me dreaming
  Of a sweet bow'd down face with yellow hair,
Betwixt green leaves I used to see it gleaming,
  A half smile on the lips, though lines of care

Had sunk the cheeks, and made the great eyes hollow;
  What other work in all the world had I,

But through all turns of fate that face to follow?
   But wars and business kept me there to die.

O child, I should have slain my brother, too,
   My brother, Love, lain moaning in the grass,
Had I not ridden out to look for you,
   When I had watch'd the gilded courtiers pass

From the golden hall. But it is strange your name
   Is not the same the minstrel sung of yore;
You call'd it Rapunzel, 'tis not the name.
   See, love, the stems shine through the open door.

*

Morning in the woods.
RAPUNZEL:

O Love! me and my unknown name you have well won;
   The witch's name was Rapunzel; eh! not so sweet?
No!—but is this real grass, love, that I tread upon?
   What call they these blue flowers that lean across
     my feet?

THE PRINCE:

Dip down your dear face in the dewy grass, O love!
   And ever let the sweet slim harebells, tenderly hung,
Kiss both your parted lips; and I will hang above,
   And try to sing that song the dreamy harper sung.

He sings:

'Twixt the sunlight and the shade
Float up memories of my maid,
   God, remember Guendolen!

Gold or gems she did not wear,
But her yellow rippled hair,
   Like a veil, hid Guendolen!

'Twixt the sunlight and the shade,
My rough hands so strangely made,
   Folded golden Guendolen;

Hands used to grip the sword-hilt hard,
Framed her face, while on the sward
    Tears fell down from Guendolen.

Guendolen now speaks no word,
Hands fold round about the sword.
    Now no more of Guendolen.

Only 'twixt the light and shade
Floating memories of my maid
    Make me pray for Guendolen.

GUENDOLEN:
I kiss thee, new-found name; but I will never go:
    Your hands need never grip the hammer'd sword again,
But all my golden hair shall ever round you flow,
    Between the light and shade from Golden Guendolen.

*

Afterwards in the palace.
KING SEBALD:
I took my armour off,
Put on king's robes of gold,
Over the kirtle green
The gold fell fold on fold.

THE WITCH, *out of hell:*
Guendolen! Guendolen!
One lock of hair.

GUENDOLEN:
I am so glad, for every day
He kisses me much the same way
As in the tower: under the sway
Of all my golden hair.

KING SEBALD:
We rode throughout the town,
    A gold crown on my head.

Through all the gold-hung streets,
  "Praise God!" the people said.

The Witch:

Guendolen! Guendolen!
Lend me your hair!

Guendolen:

Verily, I seem like one
Who, when day is almost done,
Through a thick wood meets the sun
    That blazes in her hair.

King Sebald:

Yea, at the palace gates,
  "Praise God!" the great knights said,
"For Sebald the high king,
  And the lady's golden head."

The Witch:

Woe is me! Guendolen
Sweeps back her hair.

Guendolen:

Nothing wretched now, no screams;
I was unhappy once in dreams,
And even now a harsh voice seems
    To hang about my hair.

The Witch:

WOE! THAT ANY MAN COULD DARE
TO CLIMB UP THE YELLOW STAIR,
GLORIOUS GUENDOLEN'S GOLDEN HAIR.

The Sword Of Welleran

AFTER WILLIAM MORRIS, the second major writer in the English language to work in the new genre of the imaginary-world fantasy tale was an Anglo-Irish peer, the Hon. Edward John Moreton Drax Plunkett, who was born in London on July 24, 1878—William Morris, incidentally, was 44 at the time.

Educated at Eton and Sandhurst, he succeeded his father to the title as eighteenth Baron Dunsany when he was 21. The title, by the way, has been in the family for nearly one thousand years: it goes back all the way to the Norman Conquest.

On the surface, Lord Dunsany lived the normal life of a British peer—hunting, riding to hounds, soldiering (he served with the Coldstream Guards in the Boer War and with the Royal Inniskilling Fusiliers during World War I)—but beyond these pursuits, the usual activities of the landed nobility, he was also a gifted writer of prodigious energy. Essayist, playwright, novelist, poet, autobiographer, short story writer and translator, he produced more than sixty books before his death in Dublin at the age of 79 on October 25, 1957.

The first of these books, a collection of short fantasy tales entitled *The Gods of Pegāna*, was published in 1905—only ten years after the first of the great William Morris fantasies, *The Wood Beyond the World*. The tales in this first collection were not very promising—they contained more style than story—but they did display the remarkable imaginative gifts of a brilliant creative talent. The book constituted, in effect, a complete private mythology of the many gods who ruled his imaginary countries "at the edge of the world" or in those mysterious and little-known lands "where geography ends and fairyland begins."

Thereafter followed every two or three years a further collection of tales. *The Sword of Welleran* (1908), and *A Dreamer's Tales* (1910), and *The Book of Wonder* (1912), and *Fifty-One Tales* (1915), and *The Last Book of Wonder* (1916), and *Tales of Three Hemispheres* (1919) and yet others. In all, Dunsany produced something like eighteen volumes of short stories, although not all of them are laid in magic worlds of his own invention. There was also at least one novel squarely in the fantasy world genre, *The King of Elfland's Daughter* (1924), and many of his plays are laid in the same *terra incognita* as the tales. Incidentally, Dunsany's plays were far more popular than his stories: many were staged at the famous Abbey Theatre in Dublin, and some were quite successful—successful enough to be imported to Broadway; indeed, at one time Dunsany had no fewer than five different plays showing in New York at the same time.

Dunsany became probably the most influential single fantasy writer of the first half of the 20th Century. The American novelist James Branch Cabell read his stories and admired them greatly; the young H. P. Lovecraft was tremendously impressed by Dunsany and imitated him very closely in a dozen or so early stories, culminating in Lovecraft's most unusual novel, *The Dream-Quest of Unknown Kadath*. And the work of Robert E. Howard, Clark Ashton Smith, Fritz Leiber, Jack Vance and many another modern fantasy author displays, to varied degree, the influence of Lord Dunsany. His influence on the fantasy written during the first half of this century is more than likely to be equalled by the influence of J. R. R. Tolkien on the writers of the last half, but this is yet to be seen although early signs of a Tolkienian influence are already visible in the work of Lloyd Alexander, Carol Kendall, Alan Garner and other recent writers.

I have gone to considerable lengths to select from the

enormous number of Dunsany's fantastic tales one which is not only an excellent story in itself, but one which perfectly typifies the finest qualities of his art.

The lucent, singing qualities of his prose, drenched in a blur of hazy colors, illuminated with flashes of brilliant imagination, bejewelled with curious, exotic and evocative names, are marvellously visible in this little tale which has never before appeared in a paperback anthology, and has not been reprinted anywhere, to my knowledge, in at least fifteen years . . . .

Where the great plain of Tarphet runs up, as the sea in estuaries, among the Cyresian mountains, there stood long since the city of Merimna well nigh among the shadows of the crags. I have never seen a city in the world so beautiful as Merimna seemed to me when first I dreamed of it. It was a marvel of spires and figures of bronze, and marble fountains, and trophies of fabulous wars, and broad streets given over wholly to the Beautiful. Right through the centre of the city there went an avenue fifty strides in width, and along each side of it stood likenesses in bronze of the kings of all the countries that the people of Merimna had ever known. At the end of that avenue was a colossal chariot with three bronze horses driven by the winged figure of Fame, and behind her in the chariot the huge form of Welleran, Merimna's ancient hero, standing with extended sword. So urgent was the mien and attitude of Fame, and so swift the pose of the horses, that you had sworn that the chariot was instantly upon you, and that its dust already veiled the faces of the kings. And in the city was a mighty hall, wherein were stored the trophies of Merimna's heroes. Sculptured it was, and domed, the glory of the art of masons a long while dead, and on the summit of the dome the image of Rollory sat gazing across the Cyresian mountains towards the wide lands beyond, the lands that knew his sword. And beside Rollory, like an old nurse, the figure of Victory sat, hammering into a golden wreath of laurels for his head the crowns of fallen kings.

Such was Merimna, a city of sculptured Victories and warriors of bronze. Yet in the time of which I write the art of war had been forgotten in Merimna, and the people almost slept. To and fro and up and down they would walk through the marble streets, gazing at memorials of the things achieved by their country's swords in the hands of those that long ago had loved Merimna well. Almost they slept, and dreamed of Welleran, Soorenard, Mommolek, Rollory, Akanax, and young Irain.

Of the lands beyond the mountains that lay all round about them they knew nothing, save that they were the theatre of the terrible deeds of Welleran, that he had done with his sword. Long since these lands had fallen back into the possession of the nations that had been scourged by Merimna's armies. Nothing now remained to Merimna's men save their inviolate city and the glory of the remembrance of their ancient fame. At night they would place sentinels far out in the desert, but these always slept at their posts, dreaming of Rollory, and three times every night a guard would march around the city, clad in purple, bearing lights and singing songs of Welleran. Always the guard went unarmed, but as the sound of their song went echoing across the plain towards the looming mountains, the desert robbers would hear the name of Welleran and steal away to their haunts. Often dawn would come across the plain, shimmering marvellously upon Merimna's spires, abashing all the stars, and find the guard still singing songs of Welleran, and would change the colour of their purple robes and pale the lights they bore. But the guard would go back leaving the ramparts safe, and one by one the sentinels in the plain would awake from dreaming of Rollory and shuffle back into the city quite cold. Then something of the menace would pass away from the faces of the Cyresian mountains, that from the north and the west and the south lowered upon Merimna, and clear in the morning the statues and the pillars would arise in the old inviolate city.

You would wonder that an unarmed guard and sentinels that slept could defend a city that was stored with all the glories of art, that was rich in gold and bronze, a haughty city that had erst oppressed its neighbours, whose people had forgotten the art of war. Now this is the reason that, though all her other lands had long been taken from her, Merimna's city was safe. A strange thing was believed or feared by the fierce tribes beyond the mountains, and it was credited among them that at certain stations round Merimna's ramparts there still rode Welleran, Soorenard, Mommolek, Rollory, Akanax, and young Irain. Yet it was close on a hundred years since Irain, the youngest of Merimna's heroes, fought his last battle with the tribes.

Sometimes indeed there arose among the tribes young men who doubted, and said: "How may a man for ever escape death?"

But graver men answered them: "Hear us, ye whose wisdom has discerned so much, and discern for us how a man may escape death when two score horsemen assail him with their swords, all of them sworn to kill him, and all of them sworn upon their country's gods; as often Welleran hath. Or discern for us how two men alone may enter a walled city by night, and bring away from it that city's king, as did Soorenard and Mommolek. Surely men that have escaped so many swords and so many sleety arrows shall escape the years and Time."

And the young men were humbled and became silent. Still, the suspicion grew. And often when the sun set on the Cyresian mountains, men in Merimna discerned the forms of savage tribesmen black against the light peering towards the city.

All knew in Mermina that the figures round the ramparts were only statues of stone, yet even there a hope lingered among a few that some day their old heroes would come again, for certainly none had ever seen them die. Now, it had been the wont of these six war-

riors of old, as each received his last wound and knew it
to be mortal, to ride away to a certain deep ravine and
cast his body in, as somewhere I have read great elephants do, hiding their bones away from lesser beasts. It
was a ravine steep and narrow even at the ends, a great
cleft into which no man could come by any path. There
rode Welleran alone, panting hard; and there later rode
Soorenard and Mommolek, Mommolek with a mortal
wound upon him not to return, but Soorenard was un-
wounded and rode back alone from leaving his dear
friend resting among the mighty bones of Welleran. And
there rode Soorenard, when his day was come, with Rollory and Akanax, and Rollory rode in the middle and
Soorenard and Akanax on either side. And the long ride
was a hard and weary thing for Soorenard and Akanax,
for they both had mortal wounds; but the long ride was
easy for Rollory, for he was dead. So the bones of these
five heroes whitened in an enemy's land, and very still
they were though they had troubled cities, and none
knew where they lay saving only Irain, the young captain, who was but twenty-five when Mommolek, Rollory,
and Akanax rode away. And among them were strewn
their saddles and their bridles, and all the accoutrements
of their horses, lest any man should ever find them afterwards and say in some foreign city: "Lo! the bridles or
the saddles of Merimna's captains, taken in war," but
their beloved trusty horses they turned free.

Forty years afterwards, in the hour of a great victory,
his last wound came upon Irain, and the wound was terrible and would not close. And Irain was the last of the
captains, and rode away alone. It was a long way to the
dark ravine, and Irain feared that he would never come
to the resting-place of the old heroes, and he urged his
horse on swiftly, and clung to the saddle with his hands.
And often as he rode he fell asleep, and dreamed of earlier days, and of the times when he first rode forth to the
great wars of Welleran, and of the time when Welleran
first spake to him, and of the faces of Welleran's comrades when they led charges in the battle. And ever as
he awoke a great longing arose in his soul, as it hovered

on his body's brink, a longing to lie among the bones of the old heroes. At last when he saw the dark ravine making a scar across the plain, the soul of Irain slipped out through his great wound and spread its wings, and pain departed from the poor hacked body and, still urging his horse forward. Irain died. But the old true horse cantered on, till suddenly he saw before him the dark ravine and put his forefeet out on the very edge of it and stopped. Then the body of Irain came toppling forward over the right shoulder of the horse, and his bones mingle and rest as the years go by with the bones of Merimna's heroes.

Now there was a little boy in Merimna named Rold. I saw him first, I, the dreamer, that sit before my fire asleep, I saw him first as his mother led him through the great hall where stand the trophies of Merimna's heroes. He was five years old, and they stood before the great glass casket wherein lay the sword of Welleran, and his mother said: "The sword of Welleran." And Rold said: "What should a man do with the sword of Welleran?" And his mother answered: "Men look at the sword and remember Welleran." And they went on and stood before the great red cloak of Welleran, and the child said: "Why did Welleran wear this great red cloak?" And his mother answered: "It was the way of Welleran."

When Rold was a little older he stole out of his mother's house quite in the middle of the night when all the world was still, and Merimna asleep, dreaming of Welleran, Soorenard, Mommolek, Rollory, Akanax, and young Irain. And he went down to the ramparts to hear the purple guard go by, singing of Welleran. And the purple guard came by with lights, all singing in the stillness, and dark shapes out in the desert turned and fled. And Rold went back again to his mother's house with a great yearning towards the name of Welleran, such as men feel for very holy things.

And in time Rold grew to know the pathway all round the ramparts, and the six equestrian statues that were there, guarding Merimna still. These statues were not like other statues, they were so cunningly wrought of many-coloured marbles that none might be quite sure until very close that they were not living men. There was a horse of dappled marble, the horse of Akanax. The horse of Rollory was of alabaster, pure white, his armour was wrought out of a stone that shone, and his horseman's cloak was made of a blue stone. He looked northwards.

But the marble horse of Welleran was pure black, and there sat Welleran upon him, looking solemnly westwards. His horse it was whose cold neck Rold most loved to stroke, and it was Welleran whom the watchers at sunset on the mountains the most clearly saw as they peered towards the city. And Rold loved the red nostrils of the great black horse and his rider's jasper cloak.

Now, beyond the Cyresians the suspicion grew that Merimna's heroes were dead, and a plan was devised that a man should go by night and come close to the figures upon the ramparts and see whether they were Welleran, Soorenard, Mommolek, Rollory, Akanax, and young Irain. And all were agreed upon the plan, and many names were mentioned of those who should go, and the plan matured for many years. It was during these years that watchers clustered often at sunset upon the mountains, but came no nearer. Finally, a better plan was made, and it was decided that two men who had been by chance condemned to death should be given a pardon if they went down into the plain by night and discovered whether or not Merimna's heroes lived. At first the two prisoners dared not go, but after a while one of them, Seejar, said to his companion, Sajar-Ho: "See now, when the King's axeman smites a man upon the neck that man dies."

And the other said that this was so. Then said Seejar: "And even though Welleran smite a man with his sword, no more befalleth him than death."

Then Sajar-Ho thought for a while. Presently he said: "Yet the eye of the King's axeman might err at the moment of his stroke or his arm fail him, and the eye of Welleran hath never erred nor his arm failed. It were better to bide here."

Then said Seejar: "Maybe that Welleran is dead and that some other holds his place upon the ramparts, or even a statue of stone."

But Sajar-Ho made answer: "How can Welleran be dead when he escaped from two score horsemen with swords that were sworn to slay him and all sworn upon our country's gods?"

And Seejar said: "This story his father told my grandfather concerning Welleran. On the day that the fight was lost on the plains of Kurlistan he saw a dying horse near to the river, and the horse looked piteously towards the water but could not reach it. And the father of my grandfather saw Welleran go down to the river's brink and bring water from it with his own hand and give it to the horse. Now we are in as sore a plight as was that horse, and as near to death; it may be that Welleran will pity us, while the King's axeman cannot, because of the commands of the King."

Then said Sajar-Ho: "Thou wast ever a cunning arguer. Thou broughtest us into this trouble with thy cunning and thy devices, we will see if thou canst bring us out of it. We will go."

So news was brought to the King that the two prisoners would go down to Merimna.

That evening the watchers led them to the mountain's edge, and Seejar and Sajar-Ho went down towards the plain by the way of a deep ravine, and the watchers watched them go. Presently their figures were wholly hid in the dusk. Then night came up, huge and holy, out of the waste marshes to the eastwards and low lands and the sea; and the angels that watched over all men through the day closed their great eyes and slept, and the angels that watched over all men through the night woke and ruffled their deep blue feathers and stood up and watched. But the plain became a thing of mystery filled with fears. So the two spies went down the deep ravine, and coming to the plain sped stealthily across it. Soon they came to the line of sentinels asleep upon the sand, and one stirred in his sleep calling on Rollory, and a great dread seized upon the spies and they whispered

"Rollory lives," but they remembered the King's Axeman and went on. And next they came to the great bronze statue of Fear, carved by some sculptor of the old glorious years in the attitude of flight towards the mountains, calling to her children as she fled. And the children of Fear were carved in the likeness of the armies of all the trans-Cyresian tribes, with their backs towards Merimna, flocking after Fear. And from where he sat his horse behind the ramparts the sword of Welleran was stretched out over their heads, as ever it was wont. And the two spies kneeled down in the sand and kissed the huge bronze foot of the statue of Fear, saying: "O Fear, Fear." And as they knelt they saw lights far off along the ramparts coming nearer and nearer, and heard men singing of Welleran. And the purple guard came nearer and went by with their lights, and passed on into the distance round the ramparts still singing of Welleran. And all the while the two spies clung to the foot of the statue, muttering: "O Fear, Fear." But when they could hear the name of Welleran no more they arose and came to the ramparts and climbed over them and came at once upon the figure of Welleran, and they bowed low to the ground, and Seejar said: "O Welleran, we came to see whether thou didst yet live." And for a long while they waited with their faces to earth. At last Seejar looked up towards Welleran's terrible sword, and it was still stretched out pointing to the carved armies that followed after Fear. And Seejar bowed to the ground again and touched the horse's hoof, and it seemed cold to him. And he moved his hand higher and touched the leg of the horse, and it seemed quite cold. At last he touched Welleran's foot, and the armour on it seemed hard and stiff. Then as Welleran moved not and spake not, Seejar climbed up at last and touched his hand, the terrible hand of Welleran, and it was marble. Then Seejar laughed aloud, and he and Sajar-Ho sped down the empty pathway and found Rollory, and he was marble too. Then they climbed down over the ramparts and went back across the plain, walking contemptuously past the figure of Fear, and heard the guard returning round the ramparts for the third time, singing of Welleran: and Seejar said: "Ay, you may sing of Welleran, but Welleran is dead and a doom is on your city."

And they passed on and found the sentinel still restless in the night and calling on Rollory. And Sajar-Ho muttered: "Ay, you may call on Rollory, but Rollory is dead and naught can save your city."

And the two spies went back alive to their mountains again, and as they reached them the first ray of the sun came up red over the desert behind Merimna and lit Merimna's spires. It was the hour when the purple guard were wont to go back into the city with their tapers pale and their robes a brighter colour, when the cold sentinels came shuffling in from dreaming in the desert; it was the hour when the desert robbers hid themselves away, going back to their mountain caves, it was the hour when gauze-winged insects are born that only live for a day, it was the hour when men die that are condemned to death, and in this hour a great peril, new and terrible, arose for Merimna and Merimna knew it not.

Then Seejar turning said: "See how red the dawn is and how red the spires of Merimna. They are angry with Merimna in Paradise and They bode its doom."

So the two spies went back and brought the news to their king, and for a few days the kings of those countries were gathering their armies together; and one evening the armies of four kings were massed together at the top of the deep ravine, all crouching below the summit waiting for the sun to set. All wore resolute and fearless faces, yet inwardly every man was praying to the gods, unto each one in turn.

Then the sun set, and it was the hour when the bats and the dark creatures are abroad and the lions come down from their lairs, and the desert robbers go into the plains again and fevers rise up winged and hot out of chill marshes, and it was the hour when safety leaves the thrones of kings, the hour when dynasties change. But in the desert the purple guard came swinging out of Merimna with their lights to sing of Welleran, and the sentinels lay down to sleep.

Now, into Paradise no sorrow may ever come, but may only beat like rain against its crystal walls, yet the souls of Merimna's heroes were half aware of some sorrow far away as some sleeper feels that someone is chilled and cold, yet knows not in his sleep that it is he. And they fretted a little in their starry home. Then unseen there drifted earthward across the setting sun the souls of Welleran, Soorenard, Mommolek, Rollory, Akanax, and young Irain. Already when they reached Merimna's ramparts it was just dark, already the armies of the four kings had begun to move, jingling, down the deep ravine. But when the six warriors saw their city again, so little changed after so many years, they looked towards her with a longing that was nearer to tears than any that their souls had known before, crying to her:

"O Merimna, our city: Merimna, our walled city.

"How beautiful thou art with all thy spires, Merimna. For thee we left the earth, its kingdoms and little flowers, for thee we have come away for a while from Paradise.

"It is very difficult to draw away from the face of God —it is like a warm fire, it is like dear sleep, it is like a great anthem; yet there is a stillness all about it, a stillness full of lights.

"We have left Paradise for a while for thee, Merimna.

"Many women have we loved, Merimna, but only one city.

"Behold now all the people dream, all our loved people. How beautiful are dreams! In dreams the dead may live, even the long dead and the very silent. Thy lights are all sunk low, they have all gone out, no sound is in thy streets. Hush! Thou art like a maiden that shutteth up her eyes and is asleep, that draweth her breath softly and is quite still, being at ease and untroubled.

"Behold now the battlements, the old battlements. Do men defend them still as we defended them? They are worn a little, the battlements," and drifting nearer they peered anxiously. "It is not by the hand of man that they are worn, our battlements. Only the years have done it and indomitable Time. Thy battlements are like the girdle of a maiden, a girdle that is round about her. See now the dew upon them, they are like a jewelled girdle.

"Thou art in great danger, Merimna, because thou art so beautiful. Must thou perish tonight because we no more defend thee, because we cry out and none hear us, as the bruised lilies cry out and none have known their voices?"

Thus spake those strong-voiced, battle-ordering captains, calling to their dear city, and their voices came no louder than the whispers of little bats that drift across the twilight in the evening. Then the purple guard came near, going round the ramparts for the first time in the night, and the old warriors called to them, "Merimna is in danger! Already her enemies gather in the darkness." But their voices were never heard, because they were only wandering ghosts. And the guard went by and passed unheeding away, still singing of Welleran.

Then said Welleran to his comrades: "Our hands can hold swords no more, our voices cannot be heard, we are stalwart men no longer. We are but dreams, let us go among dreams. Go all of you, and thou too, young Irain, and trouble the dreams of all the men that sleep, and urge them to take the old swords of their grandsires that hang upon the walls, and to gather at the mouth of the ravine; and I will find a leader and make him take my sword."

Then they passed up over the ramparts and into their dear city. And the wind blew about, this way and that, as he went, the soul of Welleran, who had upon his day withstood the charges of tempestuous armies. And the souls of his comrades, and with them young Irain, passed up into the city and troubled the dreams of every man who slept, and to every man the souls said in their dreams: "It is hot and still in the city. Go out now into the desert, into the cool under the mountains, but take with thee the old sword that hangs upon the wall for fear of the desert robbers."

And the god of that city sent up a fever over it, and the fever brooded over it and the streets were hot; and all that slept woke from dreaming that it would be cool and pleasant where the breezes came down the ravine out of the mountains: and they took the old swords that their grandsires had, according to their dreams, for fear of the desert robbers. And in and out of dreams passed the souls of Welleran's comrades, and with them young Irain, in great haste as the night wore on and one by one they troubled the dreams of all Merimna's men and caused them to arise and go out armed, all save the purple guard, who, heedless of danger, sang of Welleran still, for walking men cannot hear the souls of the dead.

But Welleran drifted over the roofs of the city till he came to the form of Rold, lying fast asleep. Now, Rold was grown strong and was eighteen years of age, and he was fair of hair and tall like Welleran, and the soul of Welleran hovered over him and went into his dreams as a butterfly flits through trellis-work into garden of flowers, and the soul of Welleran said to Rold in his dreams: "Thou wouldst go and see again the sword of Welleran, the great curved sword of Welleran. Thou wouldst go and look at it in the night with the moonlight shining upon it."

And the longing of Rold in his dreams to see the sword caused him to walk still sleeping from his mother's house to the hall wherein were the trophies of the heroes. And the soul of Welleran urging the dreams of Rold caused him to pause before the great cloak, and there the soul said among the dreams: "Thou art cold in the night; fling now a cloak around thee."

And Rold drew round about him the huge red cloak of Welleran. Then Rold's dreams took him to the sword, and the soul said to the dreams: "Thou hast a longing to hold the sword of Welleran: take up the sword in thy hand."

But Rold said: "What should a man do with the sword of Welleran?"

And the soul of the old captain said to the dreams: "It is a good sword to hold: take up the sword of Welleran."

And Rold, still sleeping and speaking aloud, said: "It is not lawful; none may touch the sword."

And Rold turned to go. Then a great and terrible cry arose in the soul of Welleran, all the more bitter for that he could not utter it, and it went round and round his soul finding no utterance, like a cry evoked long since by some murderous deed in some old haunted chamber that whispers through the ages heard by none.

And the soul of Welleran cried out to the dreams of Rold: "Thy knees are tied! Thou art fallen in a marsh! Thou can'st not move."

And the dreams of Rold said to him: "Thy knees are tied, thou art fallen in a marsh," and Rold stood still before the sword. Then the soul of the warrior wailed among Rold's dreams, as Rold stood before the sword.

"Welleran is crying for his sword, his wonderful curved sword. Poor Welleran, that once fought for Merimna, is crying for his sword in the night. Thou wouldst not keep Welleran without his beautiful sword when he is dead and cannot come for it, poor Welleran who fought for Merimna."

And Rold broke the glass casket with his hand and took the sword, the great curved sword of Welleran; and the soul of the warrior said among Rold's dreams: "Welleran is waiting in the deep ravine that runs into the mountains, crying for his sword."

And Rold went down through the city and climbed over the ramparts, and walked with his eyes wide open but still sleeping over the desert to the mountains.

Already a great multitude of Merimna's citizens were gathered in the desert before the deep ravine with old swords in their hands, and Rold passed through them as he slept holding the sword of Welleran, and the people cried in amaze to one another as he passed: "Rold hath the sword of Welleran!"

And Rold came to the mouth of the ravine, and there the voices of the people woke him. And Rold knew nothing that he had done in his sleep, and looked in amazement at the sword in his hand and said: "What art thou, thou beautiful thing? Lights shimmer in thee, thou art restless. It is the sword of Welleran, the great curved sword of Welleran!"

And Rold kissed the hilt of it, and it was salt upon his lips with the battle-sweat of Welleran. And Rold said: "What should a man do with the sword of Welleran?"

And all the people wondered at Rold as he sat there with the sword in his hand muttering, "What should a man do with the sword of Welleran?"

Presently there came to the ears of Rold the noise of a jingling up in the ravine, and all the people, the people that knew naught of war, heard the jingling coming nearer in the night; for the four armies were moving on Merimna and not yet expecting an enemy. And Rold gripped upon the hilt of the great curved sword, and the sword seemed to lift a little. And a new thought came into the hearts of Merimna's people as they gripped their grandsires' swords. Nearer and nearer came the heedless armies of the four kings, and old ancestral memories began to arise in the minds of Merimna's people in the desert with their swords in their hands, sitting behind Rold. And all the sentinels were awake, holding their spears, for Rollory had put their dreams to flight, Rollory that once could put to flight armies and now was but a dream struggling with other dreams.

And now the armies had come very near. Suddenly Rold leaped up, crying—

"Welleran, and the sword of Welleran!"

And the savage, lusting sword that had thirsted for a hundred years went up with the hand of Rold and swept through a tribesman's ribs. And with the warm blood all about it there came a joy into the curved soul of that mighty sword, like to the joy of a swimmer coming up dripping out of warm seas after living for long in a dry land. When they saw the red cloak and that terrible sword a cry ran through the tribal armies, "Welleran lives!" And there arose the sounds of the exulting of victorious men, and the panting of those that fled; and the sword singing softly to itself as it whirled dripping through the air. And the last that I saw of the battle as it poured into the depth and darkness of the ravine was the sword of Welleran sweeping up and falling, gleaming blue in the midnight whenever it arose and afterwards gleaming red, and so disappearing into the darkness.

But in the dawn Merimna's men came back, and the sun arising to give new life to the world, shone instead upon the hideous things that the sword of Welleran had done. And Rold said: "O sword, sword! How horrible thou art! Thou art a terrible thing to have come among men. How many eyes shall look upon gardens no more because of thee? How many fields must go empty that might have been fair with cottages, white cottages with children all about them? How many valleys must go desolate that might have nursed warm hamlets, because thou has slain long since the men that might have built them? I hear the wind crying against thee, thou sword! It comes from the empty valleys. It comes over the bare fields. There are children's voices in it. They were never born. Death brings an end to crying for those that had life once, but these must cry for ever. O sword! sword! why did the gods send thee among men?" And the tears of Rold fell down upon the proud sword but could not wash it clean.

And now that the ardour of battle had passed away, the spirits of Merimna's people began to gloom a little, like their leader's, with their fatigue and with the cold of the morning: and they looked at the sword of Welleran in Rold's hand and said: "Not any more, not any more for ever will Welleran now return, for his sword is in the hand of another. Now we know indeed that he is dead. O Welleran, thou wast our sun and moon and all our stars. Now is the sun fallen down and the moon broken, and all the stars are scattered as the diamonds of a necklace that is snapped of one who is slain by violence."

Thus wept the people of Merimna in the hour of their great victory, for men have strange moods, while beside them their old inviolate city slumbered safe. But back from the ramparts and beyond the mountains and over the lands that they had conquered of old, beyond the world and back again to Paradise, went the souls of Welleran, Soorenard, Mommolek, Rollory, Akanax, and young Irain.

E. R. Eddison

In Valhalla

from Styrbiorn the Strong

THE THIRD MAJOR writer to work in the fantasy world
tradition was also British. Eric Rücker Eddison was born
in 1882 in Yorkshire, only four years after the birth of
the future Lord Dunsany, when William Morris himself
was only 48. Unlike the romantic Morris, who devoted
his life to producing Medieval arts and crafts, or the
gifted young Anglo-Irish aristocrat who lived the glamorous life of a British peer and divided his time between a
stately manor house in Kent and a fabulous 13th Century
castle in Ireland, E. R. Eddison labored all his days in
the prosaic profession of the English civil service. He
worked, to be precise, for the Board of Trade.

But beyond the staid world of dull business routine,
Eddison was passionately in love with the world of the
great Icelandic eddas and Norse sagas—perhaps first in-
troduced to them (as were so many Englishmen of the
day) through the famous pioneering translations made
by William Morris.

In 1922, Eddison produced the first of his five novels,
The Worm Ouroboros. As I said in my recent book,
Tolkien: A Look Behind "The Lord of the Rings," the
Worm is "a magnificent, full-bodied work of heroic ad-
venture laid in a robust, richly-colored world of Eddison's

imagination, which is vaguely identified with the planet Mercury, but we are not intended to take that very seriously." The novel is an incredible creation, the work of an imaginative talent amounting to sheer genius. The prose is elaborate and Elizabethan, the plot-concept truly epic in its scope and grandeur and dramatic power. The book is filled with ringing speeches, heroic battles, amazing feats of daring, superb scenes of supernatural terror and awe, thunderous battles, romantic intrigues and tempestuous passions. As a work of prose, it is slightly—very slightly, I think—superior to Tolkien, and very much superior to Morris. It became very swiftly a fantasy classic and won an enthusiastic following which includes novelists James Branch Cabell, James Stephens, C. S. Lewis and the American fantasy writer Fletcher Pratt, and such knowledgeable literary critics as Orville Prescott and Anthony Boucher.

Eddison followed the *Worm* with a trilogy of novels: first *Mistress of Mistresses* (1935), then *A Fish Dinner At Memison* (1941), and lastly *The Mezentian Gate*, left in fragmentary unfinished form at his death in 1945 but published thirteen years later in 1958. The remarkable success of J. R. R. Tolkien's fantasy epic *The Lord of the Rings* in its paperback editions has prompted Ballentine Books to issue for the first time in soft-covers Eddison's *Worm Ouroboros* and also the Zimiamvia Trilogy described above. I have therefore had some difficulty in finding a prose selection from Eddison to include in this anthology.

But E. R. Eddison was also the author of a fifth novel. Not being a work of fantasy, it is somewhat less known than his other books. But it is none the less a fine work of writing, for Eddison was simply a great master of English prose and a stylist whose equal has not been seen in our time. His death at the age of 63 robbed us of the many brilliant novels he could have written.

This fifth and most obscure of his novels is a robust and exuberant adventure in the Viking age entitled *Styrbiorn the Strong*. It appeared in 1926, four years after *The Worm Ouroboros* and nine years before *Mistress of Mistresses*. In it, he gave free reign to his passion for Northern sagas; in so doing, he produced the most stirring and powerful tale of the Vikings that I have ever read, better even than H. Rider Haggard's superb Viking novel *Eric Brighteyes* (1891), which is generally considered the best Viking novel ever written.

Although *Styrbiorn* is not a work of fantasy, I was lucky enough to discover therein a fantasy scene laid in the Norse paradise of Asgard which serves as an epilogue to the novel. I include it here ....

————◆————

F ROM BEYOND those lampless depths where the last dim beam of the last star is dissolved in the eternal dark, immortal eyes looked on Fyrisfield: the eyes of the great Father of All, sitting on an high seat that seemed carved out of coppery-louring thunderclouds, and inlaid with those colours which are on the sea at sundown, and beaded and gemmed with stars of the night. And the appearance of His breast and shoulders and sinewy arms and the great thighs and thews of Him, that were partly shown and partly veiled, was as the appearance of the vast-rearing walls and headlong naked slopes of bare rock mountains, when the grey that goes before the dawn first stirs in those unwinged heights of air, and the coverlets of cloud roll back, and darkness creeps like a garment down, and the cold and prodigious limbs seem to awake out of slumber, and from the remoteness of small and narrow valleys, deep down where men have their little dwellings a cock crows for the day. Surely to look upon the face of Him, which was ruddy like a sea-cliff of red earth where a low-wheeling sun shines fair upon it, seen against the azure of a summer sea, was to find answers to many riddles and the comfort of many fears and sorrows.

At His either shoulder those ravens of His, like two black clouds, shadowed with their wings. There was darkness about the high seat and a music passing all music imagined by the mind of man, speaking those things which no tongue can utter, but men's hearts know them. And there were shapes about the high seat and above it, titanic, unclear, without stability, mountains, and giant forms of living creatures, and sleet and snows, and bearded stars travelling, and cities depopulate, and wild seas, and dreadful wolds, and forests, and burnings, and shapes and semblances of the enormous dead: all these blown by in a mist on a mighty wind of Eternity; and save the All-Father there is none can abide the cold of that wind nor sit in that seat: not even a God, not even those grey-faced Maidens who carve and spin beside the Well which is beneath the tree Yggdrasill; nor endure to comprehend at once all things, past, present, and to come, as, sitting there, the All-Father comprehendeth them.

Now thronged the Einheriar into Valhalla, smoking from the fight, innumerable as the multitudinous clouds in a mackerel sky at eve, heroes of bliss, of many lands, chosen from many generations of men; and the voice of their talk and deep-echoing laughter was like the sounding of the sea, and they were like unto Gods in stature and seeming, and their weapons and rich apparel like to a sunset glory in a summer garden after rain.

On a sudden our Father Odin lifted up a hand, and there was darkness in heaven all save the light of the Father's face, and all they stood up and waited in the listening gloom. And now was a noise far off, like lashing rain among leaves in a forest, and with it a rolling as of thunders far away, and pale lightnings flickered afar and vanished and flickered again through the night. Very slowly at first, then with swift strides, it drew nearer, until the roar of the tempest was like the roar of cataracts fed to fury by a cloud-burst among mountains. Then lightnings streamed in rivers of molten steel and silver from the roof-beams of that hall, which is lofty as the tent of night, and the Einheriar clashed their weapons together and shouted with a shout that was heard above the deafening thunder; "Hail to the choosers! the storm raisers! Hail to the shield-mays of the Lord of

Spears, the Father of Ages, the Loving One! Hail to the lords of earth whom they bring to join our fellowship!"

Therewith, their flying steeds swooping and balancing on the gale like sea-gulls in wild weather, their spear-heads and helms of gold a-sparkle in the lightning-flare, those Maidens of Victory rode up the night into Valhalla. When their horses tossed their manes, rain streamed from them, and from the froth of their bitted mouths snow came, and hail and sleet from their nostrils. Terrible and beautiful to look upon were those riding Maidens, as fire or the ruinous thunderbolt. And each bare athwart her saddle-bow the bloody corpse of a dead man slain.

Nine times rode they on the whirlwind and the rain high in air above the tables of the blest in Valhalla; then descending did obeisance unto the Most High, praising Him and calling Him by His holy names: Thunderer, Father of the Slain, Feared One, God of the Ravens, Blinder of Hosts, the True One, the Almighty God. Then each in turn showed her chosen one to the All-Father, and craved leave to deliver him to those whose craft it is to mend that which is broken, and put out the arrow, and close up the wound, and wake the great soul to receive again its proper body, now for ever fair, for ever desirable and strong, capable of all feats and of every pleasure that belongeth to the body of man; but of pain or decay or dissolution as little capable as if a man should go about to blow out the noon-day sun like a candle, or to batter down mountain peaks by smiting of them with a straw.

Last of all, rode before the All-Father's face the Valkyrie Skogul. Like the brandishing of swords the lightnings played about her, and her black plunging horse champed flame. Yet sweet showed, even beneath the byrny, the tender division of her breasts; and her countenance was like the golden morning kissing awake the high snow summits in the spring of the year. She cried aloud unto Odin and said, "O God of Hosts, Whisperer in the Wind, the Much-Knowing, I have done Your command. Yet with some sickness of heart I did it, thinking this should add but one jewel to Your crown, O Our Father; but earth goeth destitute for the need of such, and findeth not often one such in a generation of men. Also, he died young."

But the All-Father, sitting in that seat where that wind blows which telleth of many hidden matters, bent for a while in silence His eternal eyes on that which His shield-may cherished against her bosom. Then He spake, and the sound of His voice was like the music of the evening star when deer trip lightly down the heather-sweet slopes at twilight, and the dews begin to fall.

"Frontward are his wounds, and death availed but to tighten his grasp on the sword-hilt. Be still and question me not: I chose him first I loved the best."

The Way Of Ecben

from *The Witch-Woman*

MORE OR LESS about the same time Lord Dunsany and E. R. Eddison were experimenting with the new genre of the tale of war, quest or adventure laid in fantastic imaginary worlds and lands where the gods are real and magic works, an American novelist was also contributing to the new tradition.

James Branch Cabell was born in Richmond, Virginia, on April 14, 1879, of an old aristocratic family prominent in Virginia since Colonial times. Cabell graduated from William and Mary college in 1898, taught French and Greek while still an undergraduate, worked briefly as a journalist for such newspapers as the *Richmond Times* and the *New York Herald,* but settled into the literary life very early. His first stories were published in slick, fashionable magazines such as *The Smart Set,* and his first book appeared in 1904.

Cabell's early work varies from sentimental, romantic stories of the landed gentry in and around his native Virginia to highly colored tales of the French and English courts in the days of the cavaliers. He soon became annoyed at the restrictions of writing within the bounds of known historical and geographical strictures, and struck out in new directions by creating his own landscapes and eras. In particular, he focused on an imaginary province of

45

Medieval France he called "Poictesme"; but your typical Cabellian story was just as likely to carry you all the way to Heaven, Hell, Cockaigne or the land of the Amazons as it was to remain within the limits of even his own imagined province.

As a writer, Cabell was more of a romantic than a psychological novelist, an ironist more than a romantic, and he possessed one of the most subtle, brilliant and beautiful prose styles of any writer in the history of American fiction. His subtlety, wit, polish and epigramatic, sparkling prose won him a small but enthusiastic circle of admirers—the young Sinclair Lewis, for example, or Vincent Starrett or Louis Untermeyer, or the great iconoclast himself, H. L. Mencken, who was one of the most outspoken of the early enthusiasts for Cabell and his works. But the Welsh author of supernatural fiction Arthur Machen was also an admirer of Cabell, as was the great American humorist Mark Twain.

However, Cabell did not come to the attention of the general reading public until after 1919, when his novel *Jurgen* was seized by the American Society for the Suppression of Vice and became the center of one of the great censorship trials that have been so prominent in the history of American literature during this peculiar century. Like most of the others pilloried by the blue-noses, Joyce's *Ulysses* and Henry Miller's *Tropic of Cancer* and John Cleland's *Fanny Hill, Jurgen* was triumphantly vindicated— with the usual result: it became a best-seller, because every reader in the country wanted to see what all the shouting was about.

Although *Jurgen* remains Cabell's best-known book and a sort of American classic, it is no better and no worse than any other of his half-dozen best fantasy novels, which attracted little or no attention although they contain the same sort of erotic symbolism that brought the censors howling down upon the unfortunate *Jurgen*. In fact, to my own particular taste, two of Cabell's books are distinctly better works of fiction: *The Silver Stallion* (1926) and an earlier novel, *The Cream of the Jest* (1917). *The Silver Stallion* has already appeared in The Ballantine Adult Fantasy Series, and we hope to give you *The Cream of the Jest* sometime.

Although James Branch Cabell greatly admired the short stories of Lord Dunsany and wrote a preface to the second edition of *The Worm Ouroboros* in which he praised Eddison highly, he was more deeply influenced in his own work by an older tradition than that of Morris, Dunsany, Eddison & Company. In his sophistication, his urbane wit, and in the subtle, polished iconoclasm of his style he hearkens back to Voltaire and to Anatole France—even, in some ways, to Rabelais.

The following story displays Cabell at his best, and I believe the signs of these influences will be clearly visible to the knowledgeable reader. In making this selection I listened to the advice of several members of The James Branch Cabell Society—notably the science fiction writer James Blish and an experienced connoisseur and collector of fantasy, Paul Spencer. They advised me to take one or another of Cabell's short stories, but I finally decided on this novella instead. It seems to contain all those elements of style, lapidary prose, craftsmanship and epigrammatic wit that mark the very best of Cabell, and, as well, the irony, disillusionment and romantic nostalgia that flavors his lengthier novels.

The Way of Ecben is one of Cabell's middle works. It was published in 1924, long after the major fantasies (such as *Figures of Earth, The High Place, Jurgen* and *The Cream of the Jest*) and just before *The Silver Stallion* and *Something About Eve*.

For a book some forty-five years old, it shows few signs of age, and is still spry, nimble and lively. As I think you will agree . . . .

———◆———

Prologue *as to the Warring for Ettaine*

It is an old tale which tells of the fighting between Alfgar, the King of Ecben, and Ulf, the King of Rorn. Their enmity took hold of them because they both desired that daughter of Thordis who was called Ettaine.

Two kings desired her because of all the women of this world Ettaine seemed the most beautiful. It was the blue of her eyes, that had the brightness of the spring sky when there is no cloud anywhere between heaven and the heads of men. which caused the armies of Rorn and of Ecben to meet like thunder clouds. Blood was spilled everywhere because of that red which was in the lips of Ettaine. The golden flaming of her hair burned down into black cinders the towns of Rorn and of Ecben.

Ulf's fort at Meivod, it is true, withstood all besiegers: but Druim fell. then Tarba Achren also was taken: its fields were plowed up and planted with salt. Then Ulf captured Sorram. through undermining its walls. But Alfgar took Garian by storm, and he burned this city likewise. after carrying away from it a quantity of crossbows and tents and two wagonloads of silver.

There was thus no quietness in that part of the world, because of the comeliness of Ettaine. For two kings desired her: and her color and her shaping thus became a lofty moral issue, with a rich flowering of tumult and of increased taxes. and of corruption and of swift death everywhere, and of many very fine patriotic orations.

Then in the fourth year of the fighting, the unexampled heroism and the superb ideals of the men of Ecben, which one half of these orations had talked about, were handsomely rewarded by the deafness of Cormac. This Cormac of the Twin Hills led a third of the armies of Rorn. He was paid the price of his deafness: for three maidens without any blemish in their bodies, and for four bags of blue turquoises, and for the silver which King Alfgar had captured at Garian, this Cormac became deaf to the other half of these orations, to that half of them which talked about the unexampled heroism and the superb ideals of the men of Rorn. He betrayed Rorn.

There was never a more gallant butchering than the patriots of Ecben then gave to the trapped patriots of Rorn under the elm-trees of the ravine at Strathgor. King Ulf alone was spared out of that ruined army where every other fighting-man lay in two halves, like the orations which had delighted everybody with sound principles in that part of the world.

So was it that the victory fell to Alfgar. None now withstood him. All that his heart desired he had, and he furthermore had all the forests and the cities and the sleek pastures of Rorn. Ulf, who was not any longer a king, prayed to his gods from out of a well guarded dungeon. And everywhere in Ecben, from green Pen Loegyr to the gaunt hills of Tagd, the barons and their attendants rode toward the King's house in Sorram, and all made ready for the marriage feast of Alfgar the high king and Ettaine the most fair of the women of this world.

1. Of Alfgar in his Kingdom

At the King's house in Sorram was a hedged garden, with flagstones in the middle of it, about a little fountain. It was there that King Alfgar and Ettaine would sit and talk in the clear April weather.

"Ettaine of the blue eyes," King Alfgar used to say, "It is not right that your two eyes should be my mirrors. In each of them I find myself. A tiny image of me is set up in their brightness."

"Delight of both my eyes," Ettaine would reply to him, "in my heart also is that image set up."

King Alfgar said: "Ettaine of the red lips, it is not right that your lips should be making for me any music so dear. Some god will be peering out of heaven at my happiness, and a jealousy of me will be troubling that lonely god who has not any such fine music in his heaven."

"For no god and for no heaven whatever," the fair girl answered, "would I be leaving the Alfgar that has the pre-eminent name and is the darling of the women of Ecben. For in his strong arms is my only heaven."

Then Alfgar said: "Ettaine of the bright hair, it is not right that at tomorrow's noon an archbishop will be putting the crown of a queen of Ecben upon your shining head. Ecben is but a little land; and if the brightness of the crowns of Rome and of Byzantium, and of every other kingdom which retains a famousness, had all been shaped into one crown for Ettaine to be wearing, the brightness of this hair would shame it."

Ettaine answered him, "It is not the crown which is dear to me, O heart of all my happiness, but the king alone."

"Why, but," said Alfgar, "two kings have loved Ettaine."

Whereupon the fond and radiant daughter of Thordis Bent-Neck laughed contentedly, and replied:

"Yet to my judgment and to my desires no person is kingly except Alfgar. And, as for that Ulf—!"

A shrug rounded off her exact opinion.

Such was the sort of nonsense which these youthful lovers talked upon the eve of their marriage feast, as they sat together in the hedged garden at Sorram, where the pale new grass grew raggedly between the brown flagstones, and the silver jetting of the little fountain wavered everywhither under the irresolute, frail winds of April. And around and above these lovers who were young the young leaves whispered in their merry prophesying of more happiness than a century of summers might ever ripen.

2. *A Dream Smites Him*

Now it was in the night season of his marriage eve that a dream came upon King Alfgar. Through his dreaming a music went wandering. It was a far-off music not very clearly heard, and a music which, he knew, was not of this world. But that there was a sorcery in this bitter music he knew also, for it held him motionless.

The champion that had slain many warriors lay upon his couch, beneath a coverlet of lamb's wool dyed with blue stripings, as still as a slain warrior. Upon him who had all his desires came doubtfulness and discontent. He desired that which this music desired, and which this music quested after, skirlingly, and could not find in any quarter of earth. For it was to the sound of this music, as Alfgar knew, with a troubled heart, that Ettarre the witch-woman passed down the years, and led men out of the set ways of life.

So now a woman came to Alfgar where the King lay upon his couch beneath the coverlet of lamb's wool, and with this woman came a lean red-haired young man. The woman smiled. The young man smiled also, but his face became white and drawn when he had laid the hand of this woman upon the hand of Alfgar, and when the woman bent downward so that her face was near to Alfgar's face.

She spoke then, putting her command upon Alfgar in the while that he saw her face and the bright glitter of her eyes and the slow moving of her lips. It was in this way that Ettarre the witch-woman, whom a poet fetched out of the gray Waste Beyond the Moon, to live upon our earth in many bodies, now put a memory and a desire and a summoning upon King Alfgar in the hour of his triumph.

Moreover, Alfgar now heard, very faintly, and as though from a far distance, a noise of grieving little voices which wailed confusedly. And that remote thin wailing said,—

"All hail, Ettarre!"

Then one small voice saying, "Because of you, we could be contented with no woman."

And yet another voice was saying, "Because of you, we got no pleasure from any melody that is of this world."

And still a third voice said, "Because of you, we fared among mankind as exiles."

Thereafter all these faint thin voices cried together, "All hail, Ettarre, who took from us contentment, and who led us out of the set ways of life!"

So was it that this dreaming ended. King Alfgar awoke alone in the first light of dawn, and knew that his doom was upon him.

3. The Sending of the Swallow

Nowhere in that part of the world was there any king more powerful than Alfgar. Young Alfgar sat upon his throne builded of apple-wood with rivets of copper, and his barons stood about him. Upon his fair high head he wore the holy crown of Ecben, the gift of Ecben's one god: the kingship over all Ecben was his who wore that crown. Gold rings hung in the ears of Alfgar; about the neck of Alfgar were five rings of gold, and over the broad shoulders of Alfgar was a purple robe edged with two strips of vair.

He bade them summon from the women's pleasant galleries Ettaine, the daughter of Thordis Bent-Neck, so that Ettaine might be crowned as Queen over Ecben. He bade them fetch from the dark prison that Ulf who was no longer a king.

Alfgar considered well these two who stood before him. Behind Ettaine were her bridesmaids. These maids were sweetly smiling tall girls, with yellow curling hair and clear blue eyes: each one of these four maids had over her white body a robe of green silk with a gold star upon the tip of each of her young breasts. But behind Ulf two of the masked men in red who had fetched him hither were laying out the implements of their profession, and the other two masked men were kindling a fire.

The barons of Ecben deferentially suggested such tortures as each baron, during the course of his military or juridical career, had found to be the most prolonged and entertaining to watch. But the Archbishop of Ecben took no part in these secular matters. Instead, he fetched a chair of carved yew-wood, and he placed in it a purple cushion sewed with gold threads, so that Ettaine might observe the administration of justice in complete comfort.

Then, while all waited on the will of Alfgar, a swallow darted toward Ulf, and plucked from his defiant dark head a hair, and the bird flew away with this hair dangling from its broad short bill. At that, the barons of Ecben cried out joyously. All were familiar with the Sending of the Swallow: it was a Sending well known to fame and to many honorable legends; for it was in this way that the gods of Rorn were accustomed to put ruin and downfall upon their cousins, the kings of Rorn. So every baron now rejoiced to observe the morning's appointed work thus freely endorsed in advance by the approval of Heaven, now that Ulf's gods forsook him.

King Alfgar alone of that merry company kept silence.

Then Alfgar said: "This is the Swallow of Kogi. This is a Sending of the three gods to Rorn. In what forgotten hour did these three take their rule over Ecben?"

"Nevertheless, sire," remarked the Archbishop, "it is well, and it is much wiser too, to preserve with the gods of every country our diplomatic relations."

But Alfgar answered: "What the king wishes, the law wills. And we of Ecben serve only one god, and one king, and one lady in domnei."

Alfgar descended the red steps of his throne. He unclasped his robe of purple edged with a king's double striping of vair and he put this robe about the shoulders of another. Alfgar took from his fair head the holy crown of Ecben: the kingship over all Ecben was his who wore that crown which Alfgar now placed upon the head of another. Alfgar raised toward his lips the hands of Ettaine, he touched for the last time the lovely body of Ettaine, because of whose comeliness the heart of Alfgar had known no peace now for four years; and he placed her right hand in the right hand of another. Then Alfgar knelt, he placed his own hands between the hairy thighs of Ulf, he touched the huge virility of Ulf, and Alfgar swore his fealty and his service to the wearer of the holy crown of Ecben.

It was then that, after a moment of human surprise,

Ulf spoke as became a king. But first he waved back the four masked men as they advanced to perform the duties of their office upon the body of Alfgar. The barons murmured a little at that, and the Archbishop of Ecben perforce shook his head in unwilling disapproval.

Nevertheless, Ulf pardoned the late treasonable practices of the fallen rebel now at his feet. Ulf cried a sparing of the thrice forfeited life of Alfgar, and Ulf cried, too, the King's sentence of eternal exile. Then Ulf said heavily,—

"And do you for the future, my man, go your witstricken ways in more salutary fear of the King of Rorn."

"And of Ecben also, sire," remarked the Archbishop.

Ulf said: "And of Ecben also! Moreover, do you go your ways, my man, in even livelier fear of the three gods of Rorn, who within this hour, and in this place, have defeated your wicked endeavors, and who by-and-by will be requiting your disrespectfulness toward their Sending."

The barons cried loyally, "What the king wishes, the law wills!"

But young Alfgar replied: "My king has spoken; and all kings, and all gods also, are honorable in their degree. Yet it is the way of Ecben to serve only one god, and one king, and one lady in domnei. And from that way I will never depart."

Thus speaking, he went into exile with not any person heeding him any longer. The people of Ecben had more important matters in hand.

For now was held the marriage feast of Ettaine, the most beautiful of all the women of this world, who upon that day rewarded handsomely the unexampled heroism and the superb ideals of those men of Rorn who had died because of her color and her shaping. She rewarded all these deceased patriots by crowning their beloved cause with victory, now that Ettaine became the wife of Ulf and the Queen over Rorn and Ecben.

And now likewise the altar of the god of Ecben had been overturned by Ulf's orders, and to the gods of Rorn was paid that reverence which they required. To Kuri the men of Ecben offered the proper portions of a shepherd boy and of a red he-goat, and in honor of Uwardowa they disposed of a white bull, and to Kogi they gave piecemeal a young virgin without any fault in her body or in her repute, in the old way that was pleasing to Kogi.

Thus generously did Ulf forgive that ruining which had been sent against him in vain by the three gods of Rorn, because, after all, as the King remarked, they were his gods, and his cousins too. Nobody should look to see unfailing tact displayed by one's cousins. And for the rest, these gods would requite by-and-by, in an appropriately painful fashion, the rashness of the misguided person who during that morning had interfered with their divine Sending. Ulf, for his own part, preferred to leave that impious person to the discretionary powers of an offended pantheon. Ulf desired only that—within, of course, the proper limits, and in consonance with the laws at large and with the various civic regulations of Ecben,—the will of Heaven should be done in every particular.

One need say no more (King Ulf continued) as to a topic so distasteful. Secure in their heritage of noble character and business ability and high moral standards, blessed with a fertile soil and an abundance of natural water-power, the patriots of Ecben would now press forward to put their shoulders to the plow and to free the ship of state from the ashes and overwrought emotions of war. The most liberal policies would be adopted by a monarch whose one aim was to be regarded as the servant of his people; immigration and the investment of foreign capital would be encouraged in every suitable manner; the cultural aspects of life would not be neglected, but, rather, broadened to include interest in all the arts and sciences and manufacturing enterprises generally. Taxes, for the present, and as a purely temporary measure, would be quadrupled, now that the nation was privileged to face this supreme hour, this hour wherein to capitalize, for the benefit of oncoming ages, the united energy and integrity and resourcefulness of all

Ecben, but not an hour, in the opinion of the speaker, wherein the fate of a misguided and disreputable exile was any longer a vital issue.

Thus spoke King Ulf from his tall throne builded of apple-wood with rivets of copper.

"His majesty," replied the barons of Ecben, "speaks as a king should; and we of Ecben are well rid of an unbeliever who has publicly offered any such affront to three most holy and excellent gods."

"In fact, the man's attitude toward religious matters was always dubious, whereas his morals were, alas, but too well known," remarked the late Archbishop of Ecben, as he hastily put on the goatskin robes of the High Priest of Kuri.

And Ettaine bent toward her husband fondly. All happiness adorned Ettaine: she was as fair and merry as sunlight upon the sea: each one of her beholders saw that Ettaine was the most beautiful of all the women of this world.

"Delight of both my eyes," said Queen Ettaine, "you speak as a king should. And, as for that Alfgar—!"

A shrug rounded off her exact opinion.

4. *The King Pays*

It is told that Alfgar fared alone to the dark wood of Darvan. This was an unwholesome place into which, of their own accord, entered few persons whose intentions were philanthropic: yet Alfgar journeyed toward Darvan now that the summoning of Ettarre had led him out of the set ways of life.

And it is told also that under the outermost trees of this forest sat a leper wrapped about with an old yellow robe so that his face might not be seen. Beside him, to the left side of this leper, was grazing a red he-goat.

This leper rang a little bell, and he cried out, "Hail,

brother! and do you give me now my proper gift in a king's name."

"There are many kings," said Alfgar, "and the most of them are no very notable creatures. Yet in so far that a king is royal, a dream rules in his heart: so must each king of men serve one or another dream which is not known to lesser persons."

"Do you give me my asking, then," the leper replied, with a dryness suited to his more practical trend of thought, "in the name of Ulf, that is King over Rorn and Ecben. For my hands are frail; they are wasted with my disease: and I cannot do all the destroying I desire."

Alfgar said to this leper: "Ulf is but a little king, whom my cunning overthrew at Strathgor, and whom my pleasure raised up again in Sorram. Yet Ulf is royal, in that he would not forsake his gods, for all that they had forsaken him. Moreover, Ulf is my king now. And therefore I may not deny you."

So then the leper told his asking, and Alfgar seemed unpleased. But he smiled by-and-by; and, in that grave and lordly manner which merely rational persons found to be unendurable, young Alfgar said:

"To you that ask in my king's name I must give perforce your asking. For I will not depart from the old way of Ecben. And besides, my hands have touched the hands of Ettarre, and in the touch of sword-hilts and of sceptres and of money bags there is no longer any delight."

The leper then touched Alfgar's hands, and straightway they were frail and shriveled. They became as the hands of an aged person. They shook with palsy, and all strength was gone out of the hands which had made an end of many warriors in the noisy press of battle.

And yet another queer thing happened upon the edge of the wood of Darvan. It was that Ettaine and Ulf, and all the lords that yesterday had served King Alfgar, and all the houses and the towers of Tagd and Sorram and Pen Loegyr, and of every other town which was in Ecben, now passed by this unwholesome place in the seeming of brightly colored mists. And Alfgar wondered if these matters had ever been true matters, or if all the things which Alfgar had known in the days of his wealth and hardihood were only a part of some ancient dreaming.

But the leper put off his yellow robe, and in the likeness of a very old, lean man he pursued these mists, and he tore and scattered them with strong hands. So was it Alfgar gave that which was asked in his king's name, and the fallen champion passed into the dark wood, and came near to the fires which burned in Darvan. They that dwelt there then swarmed about him, squeaking merrily,—

"The King pays!"

To every side you saw trapped kings in their torment, well lighted by the sputtering small fires of their torment, so that you saw each king was crowned and proud and silent. And to every side you saw the little people of Darvan inflicting all the democratic infamies which their malice could devise against these persons who had dared to be royal.

Alfgar went down beneath a smothering cluster of slender and hairy bodies, smelling of old urine, which leapt and cluttered everywhere about him, scrambling the one over another like playful rats. He could do nothing with the frail hands which the leper had given him, nor indeed could the might of any champion avail against the people of Darvan whenever once they had squeaked,—

"The King pays!"

Then the trapped kings cried out to Alfgar, with untroubled grave voices, and this is what the kings said in their torment:

"Have courage, brother! Our foes are little, but envy makes them very strong and without either fear or shame when they have scented that which is royal. There is no power upon earth which can withstand the little people of Darvan when once they have raised their hunting-cry, 'The King pays!' Have courage, brother! for time delivers all kings of men into the power of the little people of

Darvan. It is great agony which they put upon us, and
from all that which is mortal in us they get their mirth,
filthily. But do you have courage, brother, for to that
dream which rules in our hearts they may not attain, nor
may they vex that dream; even the nature of that dream
evades them; they may not ever comprehend or defile
that very small, pure gleam of majesty which has caused
us to be otherwise than they are: and it is this knowledge which maddens the little people of Darvan. So do
you have courage, as all we have courage!"

Meanwhile the little people of Darvan were getting
their sport with Alfgar in disastrous ways. It is not possi-
ble for this tale to tell you about that which was done to
him, for they were an ingenious race. Yet he came
through the wood alive, because upon him was the mark
of the witch-woman whose magic is more strong than is
that magic of time which betrays all kings of men into
the power of the little people of Darvan.

So he came through that wood yet living. But behind
Alfgar those kings of men that were his peers remained
secure in the dark paradise of envy, and the little people
of Darvan attended to all their needs.

Such faithful service did this little people render very
gladly to every king, because of envy: which, with not
ever failing charity, endows the most weak with nimble-
ness and venom, as though, through the keen magic of
envy, the sluggish, naked, and defenceless earthworm
had become a quick serpent; and which is long-suffering
in the while that, like a cunning sapper, it undermines
the ways of the exalted; and which builds aspiringly, beyond the dreams of any mortal architect, its impressive
temples of falsehood, very quaintly adorned with small
gargoyles of unpleasant truths, and sees to it that the imposing structure is well lighted with malign wit and is
kept comfortably heated with moral indignation; and
which is a learned scholar that writes the biographies of
the brave, and is openhanded to reward the faithful also
with lewd epitaphs; and which, with stanch patience,
follows after its prey more steadfastly than any hound
pursues its prey; and which heartens the more flagrantly

pious, alike in mosques and in chapels and in synagogues and in pagodas, with faith that all their betters are by very much their inferiors, if but the truth were known; and which is more eloquent than any angel to deride the truth; and which pleasantly seasons gossip; and which, with a consoling droll whisper, colors the misfortunes of our kindred and of our nearer intimates with agreeability; and which weaves, with a kinglike opulence, about all kings of men its luxuriant and gross mythology, of drunkenness and theft and lust; and which enlivens every human gathering so often as envy appears under some one of those lesser titles such as this monarch, perhaps over-modestly, affects when envy goes incognito among mankind as zeal or as candor or as a moral duty; and which yet retained in Darvan its dark paradise, wherein envy ruled without any check or concealment, and wherein the kings of men paid toll to the king of passions for every sort of high endeavor.

5. The Way of Worship

Now at Clioth, near that cave which is dedicated to all gods, sat a leper wrapped in an old red robe which hid his face. Beside him, to the right-hand side of this leper, lay a large white bull chewing massively at its cud: and this leper rang a little bell when he saw that which the democracy of Darvan had left of King Alfgar.

"Hail, brother!" cried the leper: "and do you give me now my proper gift, in a god's name, before your many wounds have made an end of you."

"There are more gods set over man than I have hurts in my frail body," said Alfgar. "And it may be that no one of these gods is in all ways divine. Yet is each hallowed by the love of his worshippers: and in the hearts of his worshippers each god has kindled a small warming fire of faith and of enduring hope. For that reason should every god be held honorable in his degree."

"That may be true, inasmuch as it very certainly is implausible," the leper replied. "Nevertheless, you did not hold honorable the gods of Rorn. And, besides, I cry to you in the name of the god of Ecben."

"He is but a little god, a well-nigh forgotten god," said Alfgar. "I retain no longer any faith in him, and that hope which he kindled is dead a great while since. Yet this god also is made holy by the love of his worshippers, whom I too loved. This god who has gone out of my mind keeps, none the less, his shrine in my deep heart. So in his name I grant your asking."

"Do you give me, then," said the leper, "those golden rings which glitter in your ears."

"Very willingly," said Alfgar, for it seemed to him this was light toll.

But now the white bull lowed: and the leper nodded his veiled head as though in assent.

"—Only, now that I think of it," said the leper, "I must ask for a little more than those two gold rings. For my own ears, as you can observe, are not pierced: and unless I obtain pierced ears, then those rings will be of no use to me."

Alfgar saw that this was wholly logical; and yet this logic did not please him. Nevertheless, when the leper had told all his asking, Alfgar replied:

"I may not deny you that which is asked in the name of my own god, to whom I render every homage except the homage of belief; and I grant your asking. Moreover, I have heard the music of Ettarre, and I wish to keep in my memory the music of Ettarre, and I would not have it marred by my hearing any lesser noises."

So the leper touched the ears of Alfgar with strong hands, and the outcast King went down into the cave of Clioth. Then the leper rose, and put off his red robe, and in the likeness of a very old, lean man he went away to resume that labor which has not any ending.

And the tale says that in the cave of Clioth was not absolute darkness, but, instead, a dim blue glowing everywhere, as though the gleam of decay were intermingled here with the gleam of moonshine. Upon both sides of the cave showed a long row of crumbling altars; and every altar was inscribed with the device of one or another god.

Thus upon the first altar that Alfgar came to was engraved: "I am the Well-doer. I only am the Lord of the two horns, the Governor of all living, and the Conqueror of every land."

But upon the next altar you read: "I am the Beneficent. I ordained created things from the beginning. There is no other god save me, who am the giver of winds to all nostrils, and the bestower of delight and ruin to every person."

The device upon an altar of square-hewn granite said: "I am that I am. I am a jealous god: my thoughts are tempests. Thou shall have no other god before me."

Yet upon an altar of green malachite carved with four skulls was written: "I am the Warrior, the far-darting Slayer of all life and the Slayer of death also. No other god is my peer: through me the sun is risen, and I alone reign over the place were all roads meet."

Such were the devices upon these altars, and upon yet other altars showed yet other devices, but no living man might say to what gods any of these altars had been erected, for all these gods had passed down into Antan long ago. And about each of these altars yet knelt the ghosts of the dead, still worshipping where no god was, because in every age is born, to the troubling of that age, a man, or it may be two men, who will not forsake their gods.

So in that dim blue gleaming did Alfgar come to the ruined altar of the god of Ecben. He knelt there, among ghosts of all which once had been most dear to Alfgar. Beside him knelt his sister Gudrun, who had died when they both were children. Hilda also was there, and young Gamelyn. Yonder knelt Alfgar's father—superb and slightly dull-witted, and more great-hearted than any person was nowadays,—punctiliously intent upon his religious duties, as became a properly reared monarch of the old school. And beside the father of Alfgar that long-dead queen who had been Alfgar's mother now turned toward her son that proud and tender gazing which he so well remembered.

But she did not remember. There was no recognition in the eyes of Alfgar's mother as she seemed to look beyond and through that Alfgar who was not any longer the King of Ecben, but only an aging vagabond upon whom was the mark of the witch-woman.

And a vague host of other persons whom he had known and loved, at Sorram and at Tagd, when Alfgar lived as a boy, knelt there in a blue gleaming. All these were wavering pale phantoms, and none of them was aware of Alfgar. These ghosts all gazed beyond and through him, as though he too were a ghost, in the while that they worshipped. Thus did they all keep faith, unthriftily, with that god who now had no gifts for his faithful, and who could aid them no longer, and whom no living person honored any more save only Alfgar, who knew that he knelt among the dead to honor a dead god.

"O little god of Ecben," Alfgar said, "it is right that I should bring to you an unthrifty giving of pity and of love and of all reverence. It is needful that I should not forsake you. It is very certain that in no quarter of this earth may I find any god whom I can serve true-heartedly save you alone. For to the North reigns Odin; Zeus triumphs in the South; and Siva holds the East. To the West rule Kuri and Uwardowa, and Kogi also, who are Three in One. And the power of these gods is known, where your forever-ended power is not known any longer, and where your name is forgotten."

Then Alfgar made a lament, and this is what Alfgar said:

"It is known that Odin dwells in the North, at Gladsheim, under a roof of silver, in a fair grove wherein the foliage of each tree is golden. All that which has been or will ever be is revealed to Odin, for this god has drunk, from out of a bronze kettle, the blood of a dwarf intermingled with rum and honey. Therefore does Odin govern all things, and the other gods of the North obey him as their father. He has nine and forty names, and under each name a nation prays to him. The power of Odin is very great.

"And it is known that Zeus holds Olympus in the South. He carries in his hand a thunderbolt, and an eagle attends him. The other gods of the South obey Wide-seeing Zeus as their father. The young women of the South obey him also, and he begets upon them heroes, but his heart is given to the boy Ganymede. Ganymede and yet other nimble, half-frightened boys obey this Zeus whose love fondles them. This Zeus is worshipped in the form of a ram because of his not ever tiring lustiness in all natures of love. In fornication, as in all other matters, the power of Zeus is very great.

"And it is known also that in the East three-headed Siva has reared his dwelling place among broad shining pools of water in which grow red and blue and white lotus flowers. He rules there, seated upon a tiger's skin, upon a throne as glorious as is the midday sun. The other gods of the East obey this Siva as their father and their overlord. Whensoever it pleases him to do so, three-headed Siva descends from the brightness and the fragrance of his heaven to run howling about this earth in the appearance of a naked madman, besmeared with ashes and attended by starved demons and gray ghosts, for the power of Siva is very great.

"These things are known to all the pious that thrive in the North and in the South and in the East. My mind has knowledge of these things. My heart does not heed them."

Then Alfgar laid his shriveled hands upon the altar which was before him, and he bowed down his gray head so that it rested upon this ruined altar, in the while that Alfgar went on speaking his lament.

"For in the West, in my own West, it is known that the gods of Rorn have taken their rule over Ecben. From green Pen Loegyr to the gaunt hills of Tagd, where once a boy lived in fond sheltered happiness, the power of these three is supreme. Where once you reigned, O little god of Ecben, now these three reign, and they have honor. The burning of much incense blinds them; the men of Ecben bring to them red he-goats and white bulls and virgins; the needs of these three gods are duly served where your name is not remembered.

"These things are known. These things are known to every person, O little god of Ecben! But it is not known, O very dear, dead Lord, in what hour and in what place the power went out of you, nor in what tomb you sleep discrowned and forgotten. O little god of Ecben, whom no other man remembers any longer, my pity and fond reverence, and my great love also, now go a-questing after you through the darkness of your unknown grave."

It was in this fashion that, in the faith-haunted cave of Clioth, Alfgar worshipped unthriftily the dead god of Ecben.

Now came toward Alfgar seven creatures having the appearance of jackals, save that each one of them wore spectacles. Such were they whose allotted work it was to discourage the worship of dead gods. Each raised a leg against the altar of the god of Ecben.

When they had finished with that task, these seven remarked, because of their sturdy common-sense:

"This man attempts to preserve the sentiments of Ecben without any of the belief which begot them. This man yet kneels before an altar which his own folly has dishonored, and he yet clings to that god in whom he retains no faith."

After that they carried Alfgar far deeper down into the cave of Clioth: and quietly, in entire darkness, they dealt with him as was their duty. But his life they spared, by howsoever little, and howsoever unwillingly, because upon this aging and frail wanderer they found the mark of the witch-woman whose magic is more strong than is that magic of time which overthrows the altar of every god.

6. The Last Giving

Now at the farther end of the cave of Clioth you come again into gray daylight and to a leper who waited there in a black robe, which hid his face, but did not hide the glittering of the gold rings which hung in this leper's ears.

A flock of small birds arose from the dead grass about his feet, and flew away with many swirls and cheepings: you saw that they were swallows. A dark snake glided out from between his feet, and flickeringly passed down into the cave of Clioth, now that this leper rang a little bell.

"Hail, brother!" cried the leper; "and do you give me now my proper gift in a lady's name, before your feebleness and your wounds, and your great age also, have quite done with their thriving work."

"I once had more of ladies than I had of ills," replied Alfgar, "in the fine days when I was the darling of the women of Ecben, and no summoning had been put upon me. For in that far-off season it was I who summoned. I summoned with the frank gaze of a king who does not need to speak his desire: and out of hand a blush and a bridling answered me. So there was Cathra, and Olwen, and Guen, and Hrefna, and Astrid also; there was Lliach of the Bright Breast, and there was Una that was queen over the War Women of Mel; and there were yet others, before the coming of Ettaine. To each of these dear maids my heart was given at one time or another time: and in return they did not deny me their lips."

The leper spoke as if with doubtfulness, saying, "Nevertheless, it is better not to remain content with lip service."

"To many ladies of romance and of legend," Alfgar continued, now that his mind was upon this matter, "has my heart been given likewise; and those queens who

·uled most notably in the world's youth have ruled also
in my heart, because it is the way of Ecben to know that
every woman is holy and more fine than a man may ever
be—"

To that the leper answered, without any least doubtfulness, saying,—

"Stuff and nonsense!"

"—And moreover," Alfgar said, with the quiet pertinacity of an aged person, "it is the way of youth to desire
that which cannot ever be attained."

"These reflections appear as handsome as they are ir-
relevant," the leper returned. "Now that you have done
with your foolish talking, I cry to you for my proper gift,
in the name of no harem, but in the name of Ettarre."

"And in that most dear name," said Alfgar, "I grant
all askings."

So then the leper told his asking, and Alfgar sighed.
Yet, in the grave and lordly manner of Alfgar, which
merely rational persons found to be unendurable, decrepit Alfgar said:

"I will not depart from the old way of Ecben. Therefore I may not deny to anybody that which is asked in
the name of my lady in domnei. And indeed, it may be
that I shall make shift well enough, even so. For I have
seen the face of Ettarre, and I desire only to retain my
loyal memories of that beauty which had in it not any
flaw."

The leper replied, "Loyalty is a fine jewel; yet many
that wear it die beggars."

When he said that, he touched the eyes of Alfgar, and
Alfgar fared onward. But the leper arose, and put off his
black robe, and from behind the rock upon which he had
been sitting he took up the most sharp of scythes and
the oldest of all hour glasses.

Then this very old, lean man cried out "Oho!" and yet
again he cried "Oho!" and, after that, he went away
chuckling, and this is what he was saying:

"I have well repaired the hurt honor of the gods of
Rom. I have well dealt with this Alfgar who, because of
his fond notions, has yielded up to me willingly that

which other men give perforce. For I take my toll from all. There is no youth which I do not lead into corruption; there is no loveliness but becomes my pillage; and man's magnanimity begets no bustlings which I do not make quiet by-and-by. I chill faith. I teach hope to deride itself. I parch charity. The strong cities, which withstand the battalions and the arbalests and the scaling ladders, may not withstand me. I play with kingdoms. Oho, but I play with every kingdom as I played with Atlantis and with Chaldea and with Carthage and with Troy. I break my playthings. I ignore neither the duke nor the plowman. All withers under my touch, and is not remembered any longer anywhere upon earth."

After that, the old man said:

"The earth itself I waste away into a cinder adrift in that wind which fans the flickering of the stars. I know this assuredly; for my skill is proved; and in heaven I keep always before me the cold, quiet moon as a model of what I mean to make of this earth. Oho, and in heaven also, all gods observe me with the alert eyes which rabbits turn toward the hound who is not yet upon their scent. They know that I alone exalt the Heavenly Ones, and that for some while I humor them, as I today have humored the vexed minds of the gods of Rorn. Yet these Heavenly Ones well know what in the end I shall make of their omnipotence. Let Ruri and Uwaydowa, and Kogi also, have a care of my industry! The road behind me is littered with despoiled temples. The majesty of many gods is the dust in that roadway."

And this very old, lean man said likewise:

"But the road before me, oho, but the road before me, is obscure. Its goal is not known. If there be any purpose anywhere in my all-ruining labor, it is not known. Yet if that power exists, and if that purpose and that goal have been set, I pray that these may end my endless laboring by-and-by, for I am old, and I tire of time's ruining, and there is no joy to be got out of my laboring."

7. *Of Alfgar in the Grayness*

It is told that infirm old Alfgar passed on a gray road beneath gray skies, and about him blew that wind which fans the flickering of the stars. The woman whom he met there was gray and fat as a fed coffin worm. She mumbled, between toothless gums,—

"Tarry! for I am that Cathra who was your first love."

And it is told also that the second woman he met was gray and lean. A piping voice came out of her lank quivering jaws, and that voice said,—

"Tarry! for I am Olwen whom you loved with your whole heart."

Then Hrefna, and Guen, and Lliach, and Astrid, and Una, and all the other most dear maids that Alfgar had followed after in his youth, cried out their willingness to reward his love. Ettaine came also, bent and infirm and gray; her withered hands trembled, and her guts rumbled rattlingly, in the while that Ettaine was saying,—

"Tarry, delight of both my eyes!"

For youth had gone out of these maidens; the years had pilfered their sweet colorings; and time had so nibbled away every part of their comeliness, that these were gray and decayed old harridans who leered and cackled and broke wind as each plucked at Alfgar's ragged sleeve in the windy grayness.

The gaunt tall King trudged onward.

But here, the gray way was littered to the right hand and to the left hand with a scattering of papers which flutteringly rose up in the persistent wind; and these also spoke with Alfgar.

"Tarry! for I am Oriana, the most faithful and most fair of all women," was the first thin whispering that the old King heard: "but Amadis is far from this place, so let us quickly take our glad fill of love."

Then another paper rustled: "I am Aude. Roland

loved me until his death, and it was of Roland's death that I died; yet for your dear love's sake I live again."

And a third paper lisped: "I am Yseult, Mark's queen. But I loved a harper, and the music of this Tristram made all my life a music. Not even death might still that music, for our names endure as one song that answers to another song. Yet Alfgar now is my one love."

He saw then that upon these papers were very crudely drawn the figures of women, in old and faded colors; and he so knew that he was being wooed by the fairest ladies of romance and of legend. These swept about him futilely, adrift in the wind which fans the flickering of the stars: and all these paper figures were smutched with the thumb marks and the fly droppings and the dim grime of uncountable years. So did they pass as tatterings of soiled, splotched paper in which time had left no magic and no warmth and no beauty.

Alfgar sighed: but he went onward.

Then skeletons came crying out to Alfgar. And the first skeleton said:

"Tarry! for I am Cleopatra, I am that one Cleopatra whose name yet lives. All the large world lay in this little hand, as my plaything. I ruled the South and the North. I ruled merrily, as befitted the daughter of Rā, the Lord of Crowns, and the well beloved of Amen-Rā the Lord of the Throne of the Two Lands. The war drums and the shoutings of the legions under their tall crests of red horsehair could not prevail against the sweetness of my laughter: with one kiss I conquered Cæsar, and all his army. Then Antony brought me new kingdoms, and with each of these, and with him also, I played as I desired, at the price of another kiss. But my third lover was more wise and cold than were these Roman captains, and I died of his kissing, because that dusty-colored, horned worm was too fiercely enamored of my loveliness."

The gaunt tall King trudged onward.

And another skeleton cried out: "Nay, do you tarry instead with me. For I am that Magdalene whose body was as a well builded market-place from which men got all their desires. My love was very liberal: my love was a highway upon which glad armies marched in triumph: my love was a not ever ending festival where new guests come and go. Then a god passed, saying, 'Love ye one another.' But I stayed perverse, for after that time I loved him alone. In the hour of his tortured dying I did not leave him: when he returned from death I, and I only, awaited him, at the door of the gray tomb, at dawn, beneath the olive-trees, where the birds chattered with a surprising sweetness. But his voice was more sweet than theirs. Whithersoever he went, there I too must be: and for that reason he was followed by many who were enamored of my loveliness."

Alfgar sighed: but he went onward.

Then yet a third skeleton said: "It were far better that you should tarry with me. For I am Balkis; Sheba bore me, from out of the womb of an antelope; and in all the ways of love I was skilled. My skill was spoken of throughout the happy land between Negrân and Ocelis. King Scharabel chose me to be his queen because of that fine skill I had; and I rewarded him with a sharp troth-plighting. With one dagger thrust I took from him his kingdom and his life also. But it was in a bed builded of gold and carved with triangles that I conquered yet another king, when Solomon shaved from my legs three hairs, and I took away from him all his wisdom. So did he worship Eblis and Milcom after that midnight, because I served these gods very wantonly in their high places, and the lewd itching Jew was enamored of my loveliness."

But Alfgar put aside the lipless mouth, and all the other mouldering cold bones, of wise Balkis, also.

In such fashion did these skeletons, and yet other grinning small skeletons, flock after the tall wanderer and cry out to him. The sweetings of Greece and of Almayne and of Persia forgathered in that endless grayness with the proud whores of the Merovingians and of the Pharaohs, and each of these luxurious women wooed Alfgar. The empresses of Rome and of Byzantium came likewise: the czarinas of Muscovy and the sultanas of

Arabia attended him. The head-wives of the Caziques and of the Incas, the nieces of the Popes, and the maharanees of the Great Khans, all flocked about King Alfgar: and all were mouldy bones, in their torn and rotted gravecloths. Then from the mire along the gray roadway arose the voices of the queens of Assyria and of Babylon, who now were scattered dust and horse dung. All these, whom time had done with, now cried out wooingly to Alfgar.

But infirm old Alfgar went onward without heeding any of them, for so strong was the magic which Ettarre had put upon him that all these who once had been the fairest of the women of this world no longer seemed desirable. He came thus, in the grayness, toward a garden.

At the gate of this garden, beside the lingham post which stood there in eternal erection, sat a young man who was diverting himself by whittling, with a small green-handled knife, a bit of cedar-wood into the quaint shaping which that post had. His hair was darkly red: and now, as he regarded Alfgar with brown and wide-set eyes, the face of this tall boy was humorously grave, and he nodded now, as the complacent artist nods who looks upon his advancing work and finds all to be near his wishes.

"Time has indeed laid hold of you with both hands," said this youngster, "and the touch of time does more than the club of Hercules. It is not the Alfgar who had the pre-eminent name that I am seeing, but only a frail and half-blinded and deaf vagabond."

"Nevertheless," said Alfgar, and even now he spoke in that grave and lordly manner which when Alfgar spoke from a throne had annoyed the more human of his hearers, "nevertheless, I have not departed from the old way of Ecben."

"I know that way," the boy replied. "It is a pretty notion to have but one king and one god and, above both of them, one lady. Oh, yes, it is a most diverting notion, and a very potent drug, to believe that these three are holy and all-important. I too have got diversion from that notion, in my day."

The boy shook his red curls; and he said, shruggingly: "But no toy lasts forever. And out of that notion also time has taken the old nobleness and the fine strength."

Then Alfgar asked, "But what do you do here who wait in this gray place like a sentinel?"

The boy replied: "I do that which I do in every place. Here also, at the gateway of that garden into which time has not yet entered, I fight with time my ever-losing battle, because to do that diverts me."

He smiled: but Alfgar did not smile.

"To be seeking always for diversion, sir," said Alfgar, with a king's frankness, "is an ignoble way of living."

"Ah, but then," the boy answered him, "I fight against the gluttony of time with so many very amusing weapons,—with gestures and with three attitudes and with charming phrases; with tears, and with tinsel, and with sugar-coated pills, and with platitudes slightly regilded. Yes, and I fight him also with little mirrors wherein gleam confusedly the corruptions of lust, and ruddy loyalty, and a bit of moonshine, and the pure diamond of the heart's desire, and the opal cloudings of human compromise: but, above all, I fight that ravening dotard with the strength of my own folly."

"I do not understand these foolish sayings," Alfgar returned. "Yet I take you to be that Horvendile who is the eternal playfellow of my lady in domnei—"

"But I," the boy answered, "I take it that I must be the eternal playfellow of time. For piety and commonsense and death are rightfully time's toys: and it is with these three that I divert myself."

Alfgar said: "Your talking is a piddling way of talking. I must tell you frankly, Messire Horvendile, for your own good, that such frivolousness is unbecoming in an immortal."

The boy laughed, without any mirth, at the old vagabond's old notions. "Then I must tell you," said Horvendile, "that my immortality has sharp restrictions. For it is at a price that I pass down the years, as yet, in eternal union with the witch-woman whose magic stays—as yet —more strong than is the magic of time. The price is that I only of her lovers may not ever hope to win Ettarre. This merely is permitted me: that I may touch the hand of Ettarre in the moment that I lay that hand in the hand of her most recent, foredoomed lover. I give, who may not ever take."

But Horvendile laughed at that, too, still without any gaiety. He then added:

"So do I purchase an eternally unfed desire against which time as yet remains powerless."

"But I, sir, go to take my desires, as becomes an honest chevalier," said Alfgar, very resolutely, as the infirm old King now passed beyond this fribbling and insane immortal.

The boy replied to him: "That well may be. Yet how does that matter, either,—by-and-by—in a world wherein the saga of every man leads to the same. Explicit?"

But Horvendile got no answer to this question, at this season, nor at any other season. So by-and-by he gave to this question a fine place among those other platitudes which he had regilded slightly in the while that Horvendile waited in the grayness, and about him was moving the persistent wind which fans the flickering of the stars.

And infirm old Alfgar went onward, beyond the lingham post, into the garden which is between dawn and sunrise.

8. How the King Triumphed

It is told that all loveliness endured in this garden whereinto time had not yet entered. It is told that, advancing wearily through the first glow of dawn, Alfgar now passed into the spring of a year which was not registered upon any almanac. Here youth, as always, lived for the passing moment: the difference here was that the moment did not pass. And it is told also that this everabiding moment was that moment wherein the spring dawn promises a day more fair than any day may ever be, and when the young leaves whisper in their merry prophesying of more happiness than a century of summers might ever ripen.

But Alfgar was no longer in the prime of his youth. To every side of him, through the first glow of dawn, young persons walked in couples, and they were glad because they knew that the world was their plaything, and that their love was a wholly unexampled love which the dark daughters of Dvalinn, even those three Norns who weave the fate of all the living, regarded respectfully; and which the oncoming years all labored to reward with never-ending famousness and contentment. These high-hearted amorists, who were young, knew that time was a bearer of resplendent gifts; they knew that their love was eternal; they knew also that they were far more remarkable and more glorious than any other pair of lovers who had ever existed: and, as they walked there in couples, they mentioned all these facts.

But Alfgar walked alone: and of necessity, he looked at these youngsters with the eyes which time had given him; and it was with the ears which time had given him that he heard these chattering, moonstruck, gangling young half-wits talk their nonsense.

In no great while, however, as the infirm old King reflected, these silly children would be self-respecting men and women, and this bleating and this pawing at their companions would be put aside for warfare and housework and other sensible matters. Those interlocked young hands would be parted, the one hand to kill honorably, with fine sword strokes, in a wellbred mêlée of gentlemen, and the other hand to scrub stewpans and wash diapers. And that would be an excellent outcome: for, to old Alfgar's finding, the unrestrainedness of these semi-public endearments, through its callow feeble-mindedness, appeared an insult to intelligence.

Then Alfgar saw a woman who walked alone, upon a gravelled walkway, beneath the maples and the sycamore trees of this garden. She came toward the old wanderer, and a jangling and a skirling noise came with her, so that Alfgar knew this was indeed Ettarre. He heard again that music which sought and could not find its desire in any quarter of earth.

But the ears which time had given him got no delight from this music. It seemed, to this decrepit king of men, an adolescent and whining and morbid music. He did not like these noises which seemed to doubt and question everything. It was better to have about you much merrier noises than were these noises, in the while that as yet remained for an aging frail old fellow to be hearing any noises at all.

She was near him now. And Ettare, he found, was well enough to look at, but in no way remarkable: for to the eyes which time had given him the face of one woman was very much like that of any other woman. Nevertheless, this was his appointed lady in domnei. So the gaunt vagabond knelt, and he kissed the hands of this girl who appeared, after all, quite nice looking, in an unpretentious fashion.

He knelt because this was the Ettarre who had drawn Alfgar out of the set ways of life, and who had stripped him of all that well-thought-of monarchs desired. It was in order that he might kneel here at the feet of his appointed lady in domnei, among the very many small stones which were in this gravelled walkway, that a King of Ecben had put out of men's memory his pre-eminent name.

It was in order to be hurting his thin old knees, with these little rocks' sharp edges, that he had given up his tall throne builded of apple-wood with rivets of copper, and the King of Ecben's four houses builded of white polished stone, with all their noble furnishings, and their fertile gardens and orchards, and their low-lying, red-roofed stables; and he had given up, too, his big golden sceptre with the five kinds of rubies in it, and his herds of fine speckled cattle at Pen Loegyr, and all the pretty shaping and the bright colors of Ettaine, the daughter of Thordis Bent-Neck.

These things Alfgar had yielded up not all unwillingly, because of his magnanimous old notions. These things he had put far behind him, so that he might be following after that Ettarre whom a poet fetched from out of the Waste Beyond the Moon, to be alike the derider and the prey and the destroyer of mankind. Of all these things the witch-woman had bereft King Alfgar, and of all other things save only that dream which yet ruled defiantly in the old wanderer's brave heart.

"Thus then is the quest ended," Alfgar said, after he had risen up from kneeling upon the edges of those more and yet more uncomfortable small stones. "I have kept faith with the old way of Ecben, and with you also I have kept faith."

The girl answered: "You have kept faith, instead, with Alfgar, after your own fashion, and after no fashion which befitted a well-thought-of monarch."

Now Alfgar went on speaking with the quiet pertinacity of an old man; and he spoke, too, as though he were a little, but not very deeply, puzzled by a matter of no really grave importance, saying:

"So have I won to you who are my lady in domnei and my heart's desire. But I am aged now, and it is as your playfellow said: time has laid hold of me with both hands, and with the weak remnants of my mortal body's strength I may neither take nor defend you as befits a king of men. The music that I once delighted in seems only a thin vexing now. And my infirm eyes may not ever again perceive that beauty which my heart remembers."

The girl replied: "Yet even from the first, my friend, you followed after a music which you could not hear, and after a shining to which your eyes were dimmed. All that which other men desire you have given up because of a notion in which you did not ever quite believe. Yes: you have clung—in your own fashion,—to the old way of Ecben."

He said, "And for that reason, I am content."

She answered him with that cool and yet condoning, bright gaze which women keep for the strange notions of men. She answered him with words also, saying:

"Yet so have you raised up a brutish and lewd Ulf to the throne of Ecben. So have you tumbled down the god of Ecben. So have you lost that Ettaine for whom your love was human and convenient to the ways of men. So do you stand here, an aged outcast, from whom all ecstasy has departed. So ends the King of Ecben's questing after his vain dream, in folly and wide hurt."

He replied: "Yet am I content. For I have served that dream which I elected to be serving. It may be that no man is royal, and that no god is divine, and that our mothers and our wives have not any part in holiness. Oh, yes, it very well may be that I have lost honor and applause, and that I take destruction, through following after a dream which has in it no truth. Yet my dream was noble; and its nobility contents me."

To that the girl returned, rather sadly, "Alas, my friend, but it is an imagining at which Heaven laughs; and the gray Norns do not fulfil that dream for any man."

Alfgar replied: "Then men are better than that power which made them. For the kings of men do not laugh at this dream: and in the heart of every person that is royal this dream may be fulfilled, even in the while that his body fails and perishes."

"Yet," said Ettarre, "yet, as the strength of a man's mortal body fails, so do his desires perish also. It is a thing more sad than any other thing which men know about, that under the touch of time even they who serve with the most ardor men's highest fancies must lose, a little by a little, all hunger and all faith as to that which is beyond and above them."

He now looked somewhat wistfully into this girl's quite nicely colored and shaped face which was, to him, so like the face of any other young woman who has good health. The gaunt old man flung back his head. His white hair fluttered about in the dawn wind, untidily, and the pale-colored eyes of the tricked wanderer had a vexed and tormented shining, in the while that he said:

"It is not a true thing which you are speaking. For I retain my faith in that which is beyond and above me. I have lost the desire and the vision: but I retain my faith.

I retain my faith in that beauty which I may not see, and in that music which I may not hear ever any more, and in that dream which has betrayed me. And I am content."

The girl answered, "You speak without wisdom; for it is not permitted that any man who has heard my music should remain content."

With that, she clasped for one moment his withered hands between her hands, and the witch-woman said very tenderly:

"Most brave and steadfast, and most foolish, of all them who have followed after Ettarre, the gods do well to smile at your strange and fond imaginings. And yet, tall king of men, the gods provide for him that holds to his faith."

She touched his ears. Her finger tips fell lightly upon his wrinkled eyelids.

9. *Changing of Alfgar*

All things were changed for Alfgar. He was not any longer a frail and aged person, now that contentment had gone out of him. For all his stoical, enforced contentment had now made room for joy, because his youth had returned to him; and in that garden, now, exulted that Alfgar who had been foremost among the warriors of Ecben, the Alfgar who had been the most powerful of kings and the most ardent of lovers and the most knightly of champions.

All things were changed for Alfgar. He noted, with imperious young eyes, that lilies abounded to each side of him, and that in this garden many climbing white roses also were lighted by the clear and tempered radiancy of early dawn. White rabbits were frisking about King Alfgar. He saw that the world was lovely, and that time was friendly to all lovers. He heard a music which was not of this world, and it sought and could not find its desire in any quarter of earth. But now was intermingled with this music the sound of doves that called to their mates; and in this music he found no doubtfulness and no discontent, but only the dear promise of a life which presently would be created out of the resistless might of this music's yearning, and which would be more noble than had been any life yet known to human kind.

All things were changed for Alfgar, who grasped with strong hands the hands of the most lovely of the women who are not quite of this world. For this was visibly that ever-young Ettarre whom very far in the future the magic of the poet's love and the wizardry of mathematics had fetched from out of the Waste Beyond the Moon, to be the delight and the ruin of many human lovers less fortunate than Alfgar had been, and to elude them eternally. But Alfgar she could not elude, he knew, because of those strong hands which held her hands securely.

"The gods provide," said Alfgar, joyously, "for him that holds to his faith!"

So was it that all things were changed for Alfgar through the touch of the witch-woman who had drawn him out of the set ways of life into the garden between dawn and sunrise, and whose magic is more great than is the magic of time. And now from all quarters of the garden, whereinto time had not yet entered came young lovers, two by two, in high rejoicing.

They rejoiced because, once more, the gray Norns had regarded respectfully the importance of a sincere love-affair, and because of the oncoming years, as is customary, were laboring to reward the steadfastness of true love with never-ending fame and contentment. They cried aloud to Alfgar, with friendly smiles and with gay caperings,—

"The gods provide for him that holds to his faith!"

Then they all praised Alfgar cordially. Each couple said, with the most sympathizing kind of politeness, that Alfgar and his appointed lady in domnei were more remarkable and more glorious than any other pair of lovers who had ever existed, saving only one pair—which pair no couple was so egotistic as to mention outright.

They that had served Ettarre came also, all those maimed poets whose living she had ruined. And they said:

"Hail and farewell, Ettarre! Because of you, we could be contented with no woman. We turned away from that frank and wholesome world wherein frank, wholesome maidens walked amiably along sunlit ways. We perceived that the younger females of our kind were pleasant to the touch and were agreeably tinted. But we turned away, we blundered into more murky places, and we got deep scarrings there, because these maids were not as was that witch-woman whom we had seen and might not forget. As moths flitter after torches so did we pursue your lost loveliness, to our own hurt."

And these poets said also:

"Because of your music, we could get no delight from the music of our verses nor from any melody that is of this world. We were enamored of a music which no words might entrap or cage. There was a music which had no fault in it, as we well knew, because we had heard such music once, for a little while. But no man who lived upon earth might recapture that music. The cradle-songs of the fond mothers who bore us were less dear than was that music. The pipes and the organs and the fiddles made no such music. We heard the trumpets and the harps and the clarions; we heard the church bells; and we were not comforted."

Then these poets said:

"Because of you, we lived among mankind as exiles. The emperors and the captains perceived that we did not regard their famousness as a weighty matter. The priests and the well-thought-of sages perceived that in the while they instructed us our minds were upon a mystery, and that our thinking cherished a legend which was not their legend. So the strong derided us, and said lightly that we were wit-stricken: but, in their troubled hearts, they hated us. For we went among them as men who had drunk wine from a goblet of fairy gold: the wholesome fare of earth may not content such men: and to all human kind they became abhorrent."

Whereafter these maimed poets cried out very fondly:

"Yet we who never found contentment in any hour of our living, all we who followed after you to our own hurt, we would have nothing changed. That loveliness which we saw once and then lost forever, and that music which we heard and shall not ever hear again, were things more fine than is contentment. Hail and farewell, Ettarre!"

Such was the speaking of these poets, and so was it that they all made ready for the marriage feast of Alfgar the high king and Ettare the most fair of those women who are not quite of this world.

10. *The way it Ended*

It was now that Horvendile came likewise. As he had done in Alfgar's dream, so now did this red-headed young man smile without any mirth; and he laid the hand of Ettarre in the hand of Alfgar, in the while that the lean youngster was speaking a word of power.

Then Alfgar grasped exultingly, with his strong arms, the wife that he had won, and his lips touched her lips. It was in this instant the young face of Horvendile became white and drawn. It is not well to give where one desires.

And in the same instant the maimed servitors of Ettarre had vanished, and all the beautiful and merry young lovers passed in a many-colored mistiness. But to these had succeeded a wonder-working yet more amiable, for in this garden three immortals now sat watching Alfgar with complacence.

The largest of these smiling gods was broad-browed and great-eyed, with very long black hair and a thick beard: the robe which he wore was fashioned out of five hundred and forty and three goatskins; and with his left hand he carried a spear of flickering fire. The second god was clothed in red, striped with fine flickering lines of white; and in his yellow hair were two white plumes; between the thumb and the forefinger of his left hand he held a white bull, as yet only partially eaten. But the third god was copper-colored. He was by so much the least of the divine three that, now they all sat cross-legged upon the ground, his head rose but a little way above the taller locust-trees of the garden. About his head flew swallows. He was naked save that wrapped everywhere around his body was a darkly gleaming snake which whispered into the ear of its master with an ever flickering tongue.

Such were the appearances of Kuri and of Uwardowa and of Kogi, who were the supreme gods of Rorn. Each of them was smiling now that Alfgar had won his heart's desire. It was a great joy to Alfgar to see that these Divine Ones bore toward him no grudge, but that instead each god had lifted up his right hand, in blessing and forgiveness.

Then these gods arose and went away laughing. The power was not yet gone out of them.

It was in this way that the garden between dawn and sunrise was emptied of all living creatures save Ettarre and Horvendile; and that at their feet you saw, still faintly simmering, that which the pleasure of the gods of Rorn had left of King Alfgar.

An Epilogue as to Other Wanderers

"The gods provide for him that holds to his faith," said Horvendile, with a slow smiling. "These jealous and these rather pig-headed Heavenly Ones have very smoothly rounded off our playing with this tall, over-faithful fool: and so the saga of King Alfgar, after all, ends neatly enough."

But Ettarre did not smile. "This man was better and more fine than we are. I would that I could weep for this brave outcast king of men whose folly was more noble than is our long playing. Dear Horvendile, and why may you give me no human heart?"

The eternal artist looked sadly toward her who was the pulse of all his dreams' desire, in the while that she waited there beyond the blackened and ruined body of King Alfgar. "And why may you give me no happiness, Ettarre, such as—in this tall fool's one moment,—you gave to him?"

Thereafter Horvendile parted from the witch-woman, but not for long. For all happiness must end with death, and all that which is human must die. But Horvendile and his Ettarre, they who are neither happy nor quite human, may not, so does their legend tell us, ever die; nor as yet have they parted from each other for the last time.

And as yet, so does this legend recite furthermore, it remains their doom that he only of her lovers may not hope to win Ettarre, even though it is permitted he should not wholly lose her, as must mortal men who approach thus near to the witch-woman lose her eternally, along with all else which they possess.

Some say this Horvendile is that Madoc who first fetched Ettarre from out of the gray Waste Beyond the Moon, to live upon our earth in many handsomely colored bodies. The truth of this report is not certainly known. But it is known that these two pass down the years in a not ever ending severance which is their union. It is known that in their passing they allure men out of the set ways of life, and so play with the lives of men for their diversion. As they beguiled Alfgar, so have these beguiled a great sad host of other persons, upon whom Horvendile and Ettarre have put a summoning for their diversion's sake, lest these two immortals should think too heavily about their own doom.

To those men from whom they get their sport they give a moment of contentment. But Horvendile and his Ettarre have only an unfed desire as they pass down the years together; and because of that knowledge which they share, hope does not travel with them, nor do they get from their playing any joy. For each of these tricked lovers knows that each is but an empty shining, and that, thus, each follows after the derisive shadow of a love which the long years have not made real.

EXPLICIT

The Quest Of Iranon

ALTHOUGH James Branch Cabell was well acquainted with Lord Dunsany's short stories, and frequently mentioned them in his essays and reminiscences, Dunsanian influence on the Cabellian *oeuvre* was slight. But another American writer of the same era, the eccentric Providence recluse H. P. Lovecraft, was most deeply under the influence of the Lord of Pegāna.

Most readers know Lovecraft primarily for his later fiction, which is in the *genre* of supernatural horror. As such, he is generally considered the finest American master of the macabre since Edgar Allan Poe. But, in his early years as a struggling amateur, Lovecraft was far more the disciple of Dunsany than the pretender to the mantle of Poe.

Howard Phillips Lovecraft was born on August 20, 1890, in Providence, Rhode Island. He was a sickly, sensitive, bookish youth, and had a sheltered boyhood surrounded by doting female relatives. A precocious boy of intellectual brilliance, his early interests were geography (Jules Verne was an early favorite), chemistry and astronomy. He first encountered Lord Dunsany's stories in September, 1919, and immediately fell under their spell. Shortly thereafter, that same year, learning that Dunsany was touring America and would lecture at the Copley-Plaza in Boston, Lovecraft made the journey and heard the great fantast read from his plays and short stories.

The experience was overwhelming—cataclysmic—he was still talking about the event in his letters years afterwards. Very shortly after this ("The Cats of Ulthar" was written in 1920, and "The Quest of Iranon" in 1921) he began writing short fantasies which are extremely close and extraordinarily good imitations of the Dunsany style.

It is quite the usual thing for beginning writers to imitate their favorite authors, and certainly no reflection on their own originality if they do so. As for Lovecraft, he never attempted to conceal the fact. In a letter to Reinhardt Kleiner dated December 3, 1919, he wrote:

". . . as you infer, *The White Ship* is in part influenced by my new Dunsanian studies. There are many highly effective points in Dunsany's style, and any writer of imaginative prose will be the better for having read him . . ."

Lovecraft also acknowledged Dunsany as the source "from whom" he says, he "got the idea of the artificial pantheon and myth-background represented by 'Cthulhu', 'Yog-Sothoth', 'Yuggoth,'" etc. Thus the seeds of the "Cthulhu Mythos" may be traced to Dunsany, and probably in Dunsany's first book, *The Gods of Pegāna* (1905), a collection of short prose-poems which read like a canon of invented myths. From other writers, in particular Robert W. Chambers and Arthur Machen, he derived the notion of supporting his imaginary pantheon and invented background of myth with quotations from equally imaginary books of blasphemous elder lore.

While Lovecraft's present reputation rests on his horror tales, his early Dunsanian work is well worth the attention of fantasy readers. Here, in stories which lack the dark and morbid coloration of the Cthulhu Mythos stories, he displays an idyllic charm, a poetic flavor, a freshness and innocence of color that is thoroughly captivating. I have selected two short stories from the early Dunsanian period for your attention here. Other tales from this period, and a most unusual 39,000-word novel which was at once the culmination of this period and his farewell to the Dunsanian influence, will be published in 1970 in our Adult Fantasy Series under the title of *The Dream Quest of Unknown Kadath*.

Lovecraft died early in the morning of March 15,

1937, in the Jane Brown Memorial Hospital in Providence. He was only 47 years old, and his work was known only to the readers of the pulp magazines wherein it had appeared. But Lovecraft, a fabulous letter-writer, had gathered about him a circle of correspondents and friends, most of whom were fellow writers, and it was one of the younger of these, August Derleth of Sauk City, Wisconsin, who was only 28 when H.P.L. died, who conceived of the ambitious project of publishing Lovecraft's best work in book form. In due time a small publishing company called Arkham House was formed for this purpose, drawing its name from Lovecraft's own well-known place-name for witch-haunted Salem, Massachusetts. Two years after H.P.L. died, the first Arkham House book was in print: *The Outsider and Others,* by H. P. Lovecraft. It is very largely due to Mr. Derleth's tireless championing of his friend's work that Lovecraft enjoys his present well-deserved prominence.

Today, virtually every scrap of Lovecraft's work is in print from Arkham House. The firm, now in its thirtieth year, has devoted itself, its efforts, to preserving the work of other members of the Lovecraft Circle in print, as well as that of Lovecraft, and has published much of Smith, Howard and others who contributed to the Cthulhu Mythos. It is one of the small ironies of fate that Lovecraft, who never made more than a bare subsistence from his writing during his own life, is now a very well-known and widely-anthologized author with some fifteen hardcover books to his credit . . . .

———◆———

INTO THE granite city of Teloth wandered the youth, vine-crowned, his yellow hair glistening with myrrh and his purple robe torn with briars of the mountain Sidrak that lies across the antique bridge of stone. The men of Teloth are dark and stern, and dwell in square houses, and with frowns they asked the stranger whence he had come and what were his name and fortune. So the youth answered:

"I am Iranon, and come from Aira, a far city that I recall only dimly but seek to find again. I am a singer of songs that I learned in the far city, and my calling is to make beauty with the things remembered of childhood. My wealth is in little memories and dreams, and in hopes that I sing in gardens when the moon is tender and the west wind stirs the lotus-buds."

When the men of Teloth heard these things they whispered to one another; for though in the granite city there is no laughter or song, the stern men sometimes look to the Karthian hills in the spring and think of the lutes of distant Oonai whereof travelers have told. And thinking thus, they bade the stranger stay and sing in the square before the Tower of Mlin, though they liked not the color of his tattered robe, nor the myrrh in his hair, nor his chaplet of vine-leaves, nor the youth in his golden voice. At evening Iranon sang, and while he sang an old man prayed and a blind man said he saw a nimbus over the singer's head. But most of the men of Teloth yawned, and some laughed and some went away to sleep; for Iranon told nothing useful, singing only his memories, his dreams, and his hopes.

"I remember the twilight, the moon, and soft songs, and the window where I was rocked to sleep. And though the window was the street where the golden lights came, and where the shadows danced on houses of marble. I remember the square of moonlight on the floor, that was not like any other light, and the visions that danced in the moonbeams when my mother sang to me. And too, I remember the sun of morning bright above the many-colored hills in summer, and the sweetness of flowers borne on the south wind that made the trees sing.

"O Aira, city of marble and beryl, how many are thy beauties! How loved I the warm and fragrant groves across the hyaline Nithra, and the falls of the tiny Kra that flowed through the verdant valley! In those groves and in that vale the children wove wreaths for one an-

other, and at dusk I dreamed strange dreams under the
yath-trees on the mountain as I saw before me the light
of the city, and the curving Nithra reflecting a ribbon of
stars.

"And in the city were palaces of veined and tinted
marble, with golden domes and painted walls, and green
gardens with cerulean pools and crystal fountains. Often
I played in the gardens and waded in the pools, and lay
and dreamed among the pale flowers under the trees.
And sometimes at sunset I would climb the long hilly
street to the citadel and the open place, and look down
upon Aira, the magic city of marble and beryl, splendid
in a robe of golden flame.

"Long have I missed thee, Aira, for I was but young
when we went into exile; but my father was thy King,
and I shall come again to thee, for it is so decreed of
Fate. All through seven lands have I sought thee, and
some day shall I reign over thy streets and palaces, and
sing to men who shall know whereof I sing, and laugh
not. For I am Iranon, who was a Prince in Aira."

*

That night the men of Teloth lodged the stranger in a
stable, and in the morning an archon came to him and
told him to go to the shop of Athok the cobbler, and be
apprenticed to him.

"But I am Iranon, a singer of songs," he said, "and
have no heart for the cobbler's trade."

"All in Teloth must toil," replied the archon, "for that
is the law." Then said Iranon:

"Wherefore do ye toil; is it not that ye may live and
be happy? And if ye toil only that ye may toil more,
when shall happiness find you? Ye toil to live but is
not life made of beauty and song? And if ye suffer no
singers among you, where shall be the fruits of your
toil? Toil without song is like a weary journey without
an end. Were not death more pleasing?" But the archon
was sullen and did not understand, and rebuked the
stranger.

"Thou art a strange youth, and I like not thy face or thy voice. The words thou speakest are blasphemy, for the gods of Teloth have said that toil is good. Our gods have promised us a haven of life beyond death, where there shall be rest without end, and crystal coldness amidst which none shall vex his mind with thought or his eyes with beauty. Go thou then to Athok the cobbler or be gone out of the city by sunset. All here must serve, and song is folly."

So Iranon went out of the stable and walked over the narrow stone streets between the gloomy square houses of granite, seeking something green, for all was of stone. On the faces of men were frowns, but by the stone embankment along the sluggish river Zuro sat a young boy with sad eyes gazing into the waters to spy green budding branches washed down from the hills by the freshets. And the boy said to him: "Art thou not indeed he of whom the archons tell, who seekest a far city in a fair land? I am Romnod, and born in the blood of Teloth, but am not old in the ways of the granite city, and yearn daily for the warm groves and the distant lands of beauty and song. *Beyond the Karthian hills lieth Oonai, the city of lutes and dancing, which men whisper of and say is both lovely and terrible.* Thither would I go were I old enough to find the way, and thither shouldst thou go and thou wouldst sing and have men listen to thee. Let us leave the city Teloth and fare together among the hills of spring. Thou shalt show me the ways of travel and I will attend thy songs at evening when the stars one by one bring dreams to the minds of dreamers. And peradventure it may be that Oonai the city of lutes and dancing is even the fair Aira thou seekest, for it is told that thou hast not known Aira since old days, and a name often changeth. Let us go to Oonai, O Iranon of the golden head, where men shall know our longings and welcome us as brothers, nor ever laugh or frown at what we say." And Iranon answered:

"Be it so, small one; if any in this stone place yearn for beauty he must seek the mountains and beyond, and I would not leave thee to pine by the sluggish Zuro. But think not that delight and understanding dwell just over the Karthian hills, or in any spot thou canst find in a day's, or a year's, or a lustrum's journey. Behold, when I was small like thee I dwelt in the valley of Narthos by the frigid Xari, where none would listen to my dreams; and I told myself that when older I would go to Inara on the southern slope, and sing to smiling dromedary-men in the market place. But when I went to Inara I found the dromedary-men all drunken and ribald, and saw that their songs were not as mine; so I travelled in a barge down the Xari to onyx-walled Jaren. And the soldiers at Jaren laughed at me and drave me out, so that I wandered to other cities.

"I have seen Stethelos that is below the great cataract, and have gazed on the marsh where Sarnath once stood. I have been to Thraa, Ilarnek, and Kadatheron on the winding river Ai, and have dwelt long in Olathoë in the land of Lomar. But though I have had listeners sometimes, they have ever been few, and I know that welcome shall wait me only in Aira, the city of marble and beryl where my father once ruled as King. So for Aira shall we seek, though it were well to visit distant and lute-blessed Oonai across the Karthian hills, which may indeed be Aira, though I think not. Aira's beauty is past imagining, and none can tell of it without rapture, whilst of Oonai the camel-drivers whisper leeringly."

＊

At the sunset Iranon and small Romnod went forth from Teloth, and for long wandered amidst the green hills and cool forests. The way was rough and obscure, and never did they seem nearer to Oonai the city of lute and dancing; but in the dusk as the stars came out Iranon would sing of Aira and its beauties and Romnod would listen, so that they were both happy after a fashion. They ate plentifully of fruit and red berries, and marked not the passing of time, but many years must have slipped away. Small Romnod was now not so small, and spoke deeply instead of shrilly, though Iranon was always the same, and decked his golden hair with vines and fragrant resins found in the woods. So it came to pass one day that Romnod seemed older than Iranon, though he had been very small when Iranon had found him watching for green budding branches beside the sluggish stone-banked Zuro.

Then one night when the moon was full the travellers came to a mountain crest and looked down upon the myriad lights of Oonai. Peasants had told them they were near, and Iranon knew that this was not his native city of Aira. The lights of Oonai were not like those of Aira; for they were harsh and glaring, whilst the lights of Aira shine as softly and magically as shone the moonlight on the floor by the window where Iranon's mother once rocked him to sleep with song. But Oonai was a city of lutes and dancing; so Iranon and Romnod went down the steep slope that they might find men to whom songs and dreams would bring pleasure. And when they were come into the town they found rose-wreathed revellers bound from house to house and leaning from windows and balconies, who listened to the songs of Iranon and tossed him flowers and applauded when he was done. Then for a moment did Iranon believe he had found those who thought and felt even as he, though the town was not an hundredth so fair as Aira.

When dawn came Iranon looked about with dismay, for the domes of Oonai were not golden in the sun, but gray and dismal. And the men of Oonai were pale with revelling, and dull with wine, and unlike the radiant men of Aira. But because the people had thrown him blossoms and acclaimed his songs Iranon stayed on, and with him Romnod, who liked the revelry of the town and wore in his dark hair roses and myrtle. Often at night Iranon sang to the revellers, but he was always as before, crowned only with the vine of the mountains and remembering the marble streets of Aira and the hyaline Nithra. In the frescoed halls of the monarch did he sing, upon a crystal dais raised over a floor that was a mirror, and as he sang, he brought pictures to his hearers till the floor seemed to reflect old, beautiful and half-remem-

bered things instead of the wine-reddened feasters who
pelted him with roses. And the King bade him put away
his tattered purple, and clothed him in satin and cloth-
of-gold, with rings of green jade and bracelets of tinted
ivory, and lodged him in a gilded and tapestried chamber on a bed of sweet carven wood with canopies and
coverlets of flower-embroidered silk. Thus dwelt Iranon
in Oonai, the city of lutes and dancing.

It is not known how long Iranon tarried in Oonai, but
one day the King brought to the palace some wild whirl-
ing dancers from the Liranian desert, and dusky flute-
players from Drinen in the East, and after that the revellers threw their roses not so much at Iranon as at the
dancers and the flute-players. And day by day that Romnod who had been a small boy in granite Teloth grew
coarser and redder with wine, till he dreamed less and
less, and listened with less delight to the songs of Iranon. But though Iranon was sad he ceased not to sing,
and at evening told again his dreams of Aira, the city of
marble and beryl. Then one night the reddened and fat-
tened Romnod snored heavily amidst the poppied silks
of his banquet-couch and died writhing, whilst Iranon,
pale and slender, sang to himself in a far corner. And
when Iranon had wept over the grave of Romnod and
strewn it with green budding branches, such as Romnod
used to love, he put aside his silks and gauds and went
forgotten out of Oonai the city of lutes and dancing clad
only in the ragged purple in which he had come, and
garlanded with fresh vines from the mountains.

Into the sunset wandered Iranon, seeking still for his
native land and for men who would understand and
cherish his songs and dreams. In all the cities of Cydath-
ria and in the lands beyond the Bnazic desert gay-faced
children laughed at his olden songs and tattered robes of
purple; but Iranon stayed ever young, and wore wreaths
upon his golden head whilst he sang of Aira.

*

So came he one night to the squalid cot of an antique

shepherd, bent and dirty, who kept flocks on a stony slope above a quicksand marsh. To this man Iranon spoke, as to so many others:

"Canst thou tell me where I may find Aira, the city of marble and beryl, where flows the hyaline Nithra and where the falls of the tiny Kra sing to verdant valleys and hills forested with yath-trees?" And the shepherd, hearing, looked long and strangely at Iranon, as if recalling something very far away in time, and noted each line of the stranger's face, and his golden hair, and his crown of vine leaves. But he was old, and replied:

"O stranger, I have indeed heard the name of Aira, and the other names thou hast spoken, but they come to me from afar down the waste of long years. I heard them in my youth from the lips of a playmate, a beggar's boy given to strange dreams, who would weave long tales about the moon and the flowers and the west wind. We used to laugh at him, for we knew him from his birth though he thought himself a King's son. He was comely, even as thou, but full of folly and strangeness; and he ran away when small to find those who would listen gladly to his songs and dreams. How often hath he sung to me of lands that never were, and things that can never be! Of Aira did he speak much; of Aira and the river Nithra, and the falls of the tiny Kra. There would he ever say he once dwelt as a Prince, though here we knew him from his birth. Nor was there ever a marble city of Aira, or those who could delight in strange songs, save in the dreams of mine old playmate, Iranon who is gone."

And in the twilight, as the stars came out one by one and the moon cast on the marsh a radiance like that which a child sees quivering on the floor as he is rocked to sleep at evening, there walked into the lethal quicksands a very old man in tattered purple, crowned with withered vine leaves and gazing ahead as if upon the golden domes of a fair city where dreams are understood.

That night something of youth and beauty died in the elder world.

H.P. Lovecraft

The Cats Of Ulthar

THIS LAST story, "The Quest of Iranon," is written like a fable or a parable, and almost in a Biblical prose. However, the second of our two selections from Lovecraft's Dunsanian tales of Earth's Dreamlands is very different in style, mood and substance.

Not only is it one of the shortest and most rare of all Lovecraft's stories, but it has never before appeared in paperback, so far as I have been able to discover. So I commend it to your attention . . . .

IT IS said that in Ulthar, which lies beyond the river Skai, no man may kill a cat; and this I can verily believe as I gaze upon him who sitteth purring before the fire. For the cat is cryptic, and close to strange things which men cannot see. He is the soul of antique Aegyptus, and bearer of tales from forgotten cities in Meroe and Ophir. He is the kin of the jungle's lords, and heir to the secrets of hoary and sinister Africa. The Sphinx is his cousin, and he speaks her language; but he is more ancient than the Sphinx, and remembers that which she hath forgotten.

In Ulthar, before ever the burgesses forbade the killing of cats, there dwelt an old cotter and his wife who delighted to trap and slay cats of their neighbors. Why they did this I do not know; save that many hate the voice of the cat in the night, and take it ill that cats should run stealthily about yards and gardens at twilight. But whatever the reason, this old man and woman took pleasure in trapping and slaying every cat which came near to their hovel; and from some of the sounds heard after dark, many villagers fancied that the manner of slaying was exceedingly peculiar.

But the villagers did not discuss such things with the old man and his wife; because of the habitual expression on the withered faces of the two, and because their cottage was so small and so darkly hidden under spreading oaks and at the back of a neglected yard. In truth, much as the owners of cats hated these odd folk, they feared them more; and instead of berating them as brutal assassins, merely took care that no cherished pet or mouser should stray toward the remote hovel under the dark trees. When through some unavoidable oversight a cat was missed, and sounds were heard after dark, the loser would lament impotently; or console himself by thanking Fate that it was not one of his children who had thus vanished. For the people of Ulthar were simple, and knew not whence it is all cats first came.

One day a caravan of strange wanderers from the South entered the narrow cobbled streets of Ulthar. Dark wanderers they were, and unlike the other roving folk who passed through the village twice every year. In the market-place they told fortunes for silver, and bought gay beads from the merchants. What was the land of these wanderers none could tell; but it was seen that they were given to strange prayers and that they had painted on the sides of their wagons strange figures with human bodies and the heads of cats, hawks, rams and lions. And the leader of the caravan wore a head-dress with two horns and a curious disk betwixt the horns.

There was in this singular caravan a little boy with no

father or mother, but only a tiny black kitten to cherish. The plague had not been kind to him, yet had left him this small furry thing to mitigate his sorrow; and when one is very young, one can find great relief in the lively antics of a black kitten. So the boy whom the dark people called Menes smiled more often than he wept as he sat playing with his graceful kitten on the steps of an oddly painted wagon.

On the third morning of the wanderers' stay in Ulthar, Menes could not find his kitten; and as he sobbed aloud in the market-place certain villagers told him of the old man and his wife, and of sounds heard in the night. And when he heard these things his sobbing gave place to meditation, and finally prayer. He stretched out his arms toward the sun and prayed in a tongue no villager could understand; though indeed the villagers did not try very hard to understand, since their attention was mostly taken up by the sky and the odd shapes the clouds were assuming. It was very peculiar, but as the little boy uttered his petition there seemed to form overhead the shadowy, nebulous figures of exotic things; of hybrid creatures crowned with horn-flanked disks. Nature is full of such illusions to impress the imaginative.

That night the wanderers left Ulthar, and were never seen again. And the householders were troubled when they noticed that in all the village there was not a cat to be found. From each hearth the familiar cat had vanished; cats large and small, black, grey, striped, yellow and white. Old Kranon, the burgomaster, swore that the dark folks had taken the cats away in revenge for the killing of Menes' kitten; and cursed the caravan and the little boy. But Nith, the lean notary, declared that the old cotter and his wife were more likely persons to suspect; for their hatred of cats was notorious and increasingly bold.

Still, no one durst complain to the sinister couple; even when little Atal, the innkeeper's son, vowed that he had at twilight seen all the cats of Ulthar in that accursed yard under the trees, pacing very slowly and solemnly in a circle around the cottage, two abreast, as if

in performance of some unheard-of rite of beasts. The
villagers did not know how much to believe from so
small a boy; and though they feared that the evil pair
had charmed the cats to their death, they preferred not
to chide the old cotter till they met him outside his dark
and repellent yard.

So Ulthar went to sleep in vain anger; and when the
people awakened at dawn—behold! every cat was back
at his accustomed hearth! Large and small, black, grey,
striped, yellow and white, none was missing. Very sleek
and fat did the cats appear, and sonorous with purring
content. The citizens talked with one another of the
affair, and marveled not a little. Old Kranon again in-
sisted that it was the dark folk who had taken them,
since cats did not return alive from the cottage of the
ancient man and his wife. But all agreed on one thing:
that the refusal of the cats to eat their portions of meat
or to drink their saucers of milk was exceedingly curious. And for two whole days the sleek, lazy cats of Ulthar would touch no food, but only doze by the fire or in
the sun.

It was fully a week before the villagers noticed that
no lights were appearing at dusk in the windows of the
cottage under the trees. Then the lean Nith remarked
that no one had seen the old man or his wife since the
night the cats were away. In another week the burgomaster decided to overcome his fears and call at the
strangely silent dwelling as a matter of duty, though in
so doing he was careful to take with him Shang the
blacksmith and Thul the cutter of stone as witnesses.
And when they had broken down the frail door they
found only this: two cleanly picked human skeletons on
the earthen floor, and a number of singular beetles
crawling in the shadowy corners.

There was subsequently much talk among the burgesses of Ulthar. Zath, the coroner, disputed at length
with Nith, the lean notary; and Kranon and Shang and
Thul were overwhelmed with questions. Even little Atal,
the innkeeper's son, was closely questioned and given a
sweetmeat as reward. They talked of the old cotter and   .

his wife, of the caravan of dark wanderers, of small Menes and his black kitten, of the prayer of Menes and of the sky during that prayer, of the doings of the cats on the night the caravan left, and of what was later found in the cottage under the dark trees in the repellent yard.

And in the end the burgesses passed that remarkable law which is told of by traders in Hatheg and discussed by travelers in Nir; namely, that in Ulthar no man may kill a cat.

Clark Ashton Smith

The Maze Of Maal Dweb

❖❀━❀━❀━❀━❀━❀━❀━❀━❀━❀━❀❖

MOST OF H. P. Lovecraft's stories first appeared in *Weird Tales*, the greatest American magazine of the macabre, and, for much of its thirty-one years, virtually the only market in this country open to the writers of short fantasy fiction.

Although never exactly successful in the commercial sense, *Weird Tales* proved astonishingly durable: founded in 1923, it did not cease publication until the issue of September, 1954. In its heyday, *Weird Tales* published nearly every American fantasy writer of this century whose work was of any importance. Many of them made their very first magazine sales to *Weird Tales*. For example, Ray Bradbury was a *Weird Tales* discovery. So—of all people—was Tennessee Williams.

The golden age of *Weird Tales*, very roughly, was the period from 1928 to about 1939. During this brilliant decade, there were three writers who, more than any others, gave the magazine its unique flavor. These three were H. P. Lovecraft, Clark Ashton Smith and Robert E. Howard. Not surprisingly, the three were friends. They never actually met (Lovecraft lived in Rhode Island, Howard in Texas and Smith in California) but they conducted a voluminous correspondence, some of which—the Lovecraft portion—has been preserved in book form.

Clark Ashton Smith was born on January 13, 1893, in Long Valley, California. He lived most of his 68 years in a cabin on the outskirts of Auburn, a village some six miles north of his birthplace. In 1954, a few years before his death, he married Carol Jones Dorman and moved to another California town, Pacific Grove.

Smith was almost completely self-educated. He finished grammar school but never attended high school or college. Despite the lack of any formal education to speak of, Smith not only mastered one of the most intricate and lapidary prose-styles in all of American literature, but also taught himself enough French to translate Baudelaire and Leconte de Lisle, and enough Spanish to render Calcano and Heredia into English. His translations, in particular those from *Les Fleurs du Mal,* are considered quite excellent.

Smith was much more than just a *Weird Tales* writer. Beyond his short fiction, he was a sculptor, a painter and a poet of remarkable gifts. Much of his verse can stand comparison with Swinburne and Poe. Some of it—the poems "Nero," and "Satan Unrepentant"—could almost stand with Milton. But it is with his short stories that we are concerned here.

In all, Smith wrote some one hundred stories of various lengths, most of them for *Weird Tales.* Generally, these stories fall into one or another cycle, sharing a common setting and a common background lore. One story-cycle is laid in the imaginary prehistoric polar continent of Hyperborea; another is set in Poseidonis, the last isle of foundering Atlantis; others in the invented Medieval lands of Malneant and Averoigne. The largest of these story-cycles takes for its setting the supercontinent of Zothique, on our own earth but in the very distant future towards the end of man, in a dim aeon when science has lapsed and magic has been reborn. (Under the title of *Zothique,* this complete story-cycle will appear in 1970 as one of the volumes in The Ballantine Adult Fantasy Series.)

For his appearance in this anthology, I have selected one of Smith's most brilliant and imaginative achievements. The tale belongs to the least developed of his cycles, that of the invented planet Xiccarph. Smith wrote very few tales of Xiccarph, and I, for one, find this regrettable, because, in a tale laid in Atlantis or Hyperborea, he was bound by the preconceptions of his readers, but in this cycle he was able to give his imagination fullest rein. Extra-terrestrial settings for a fantasy tale are extremely rare. Few come easily to mind. The best example would probably be E. R. Eddison's remarkable fantastic romance *The Worm Ouroboros*. But Smith owes nothing to Eddison: Dunsany would seem a major source (compare the following story with Dunsany's "The Hoard of the Gibbelins," or "The Fortress Unvanquishable, Save for Sacnoth").

This story is exemplary of the best features of Smith's prose—darkling and mordant, lit with flashes of jewelled description, studded with exotic names and rare words, pervaded by the lillied languor and dreamlike splendor of a hashish vision. Yet even in such a tale, style does not dominate story. Smith had the poet's ear for unusual words and singing rhythms and the artist's eye for color, but he had a strong sense of the story-teller's art (which Dunsany very often seemed to lack).

Weird Tales published this story in its issue for October, 1938. It has not appeared in any anthology since then, although it was included in *Lost Worlds,* a collection of Smith's stories published by Arkham House in 1944. I have gone to considerable lengths to restore the text to its original form, and print it here just as it left the hands of its author. Smith, you see, wrote a particularly luxuriant and opulent prose which is uniquely his own. Magazine editors would tend in general to "clean up" his stories through a ruthless use of the blue pencil. I have the highest respect for *Weird Tales'* editor, Farnsworth Wright, but I see no purpose in perpetuating his changes in Smith's text. While Mrs. Clark Ashton Smith was able to provide me with the original carbons of the stories to be included in our future edition of *Zothique,* the original of this story has long since disappeared. Luckily, however, Smith published the original version of this tale during his own lifetime in a small privately printed brochure called *The Double Shadow:* hence I am able to bring you the original version . . . .

———◆———

Wᴵᵀʜ ɴᴏ other light than that of the four diminutive moons of Xiccarph, each in a different phase but all de-crescent, Tiglari had crossed the bottomless swamp of Soorm, wherein no reptile dwelt and no dragon de-scended—but where the pitch-black ooze was alive with continual heavings and writhings. He had carefully avoided the high causey of white corundum that spanned the fen, and had threaded his way with infinite peril from isle to sedgy isle that shuddered gelatinously beneath him. When he reached the solid shore and the shelter of the palm-tall rushes, he was equally careful to avoid the pale porphyry stairs that wound heavenward through dizzy, nadir-cleaving chasms and along glassy scarps to the ever-mysterious and terrible house of Maal Dweb. The causey and the stairs were guarded by those that he did not wish to meet: the silent, colossal iron ser-vitors of Maal Dweb, whose arms ended in long crescent blades of tempered steel which were raised in implaca-ble scything against any who came thither without their master's permission.

Tiglari's naked body was smeared from crown to heel with the juice of a jungle plant repugnant to all the fauna of Xiccarph. By virtue of this he hoped to pass un-harmed the ferocious ape-like creatures that roamed at will through the cliff-hung gardens and halls of the Ty-rant. He carried a coil of woven root-fiber, wonderfully strong and light, and weighted with a brazen ball at one end, for use in climbing the mountain. At his side, in a sheath of shimera-skin, he wore a needle-sharp knife that had been dipt in the mortal poison of winged vipers.

Many, before Tiglari, with the same noble dream of tyrannicide, had attempted to cross the pitchy fen and scale the forbidding scarps. But none had returned; and the fate of such as had actually won to the mountain palace of Maal Dweb was a much-disputed problem; since no man had ever again beheld them, living or dead. But Tiglari, the jungle hunter, skilled in the slaying of fierce and crafty beasts, was undeterred by the more than hideous probabilities before him.

The escalade of the mountain would have been a highly dangerous feat by the full light of the three suns of Xiccarph. With eyes that were keen as those of some night-flying pterodactyl, Tiglari hurled his weighted coil about projecting coigns and fang-like salients. Hand over hand, he went up with simian ease from foothold to precarious foothold; and at length he attained a narrow buttress beneath the final cliff. From this vantage, it was an easy matter to fling his rope around the crooked bole of a tree that leaned gulfward with scimitar-like foliage from the gardens of Maal Dweb.

Evading the sharp and semi-metallic leaves that seemed to slash downward as the tree bent limberly with his dangling weight, he stood, stooping warily, on the fearsome and widely fabled mesa. Here, it was rumored, with no human aid, the half-demoniac sorceror and scientist had carved the more lofty pinnacles of the old mountain into walls, cupolas and turrets, and had levelled a great space about them. This space he had covered immediately with loamy soil, produced by magic; and therein he had planted curious baneful trees from outlying worlds beyond the suns of Xiccarph, together with flowers that might have been those of some teeming and exuberant hell.

Little enough was actually known of these gardens: but the flora that grew on the northern, southern and western sides of the palace was popularly believed to be less deadly than that which faced the dawning of the triple suns. Much of this latter vegetation according to myth, had been trained and topiarized in the form of an almost infinite labyrinth, balefully ingenious, from which egress was impossible: a maze that concealed in its windings the most fatal and atrocious traps, the most un-

predictable dooms, invented by the malign Daedalus.
Mindful of this labyrinth, Tiglari had approached the
place on the side that fronted the threefold sunset.

Breathless, with arms that ached from the long, ar-
duous climb, he crouched in the garden shadows. About
him he saw the heavy-hooded blossoms that leaned
from a winy gloom in venomous languour, or fawned toward him with open corollas that exhaled a narcotic per-
fume or diffused a pollen of madness. Anomalous, multi-
form, with silhouettes that curdled the blood or touched
the brain with nightmare, the trees of Maal Dweb appeared to gather and conspire against him beyond the
flowers. Some arose with the sinuous towering of
plumed pythons, of aigretted dragons. Others crouched
with radiating limbs that were like the hairy members of
colossal arachnidans. They seemed to close in upon Tiglari with a stealthy motion. They waved their frightful
darts of thorn, their scythe-like leaves. They blotted the
four moons with webs of arabesque menace. They
reared from interminably coiling roots behind mammoth
foliages that resembled an array of interlocking shields.

With endless caution and calculation, the hunter made
his way forward, seeking a rift in the armed phalanx of
vegetable monstrosities. His faculties, ever alert, were
abnormally quickened by a grievous fear, intensified by
a mighty hatred. The fear was not for himself, but for
the girl Athle, his beloved and the fairest of his tribe,
who had gone up alone that very evening by the causey
of corundum and the porphyry stairs at the summons
of Maal Dweb. His hatred was that of a brave man and
an outraged lover for the all-powerful, all-dreaded tyrant whom no man had ever seen, and from whose
abode no woman came back; who spoke with an iron
voice that was audible at will in the far cities or the out-
most jungles; who punished the rebellious and the dis-
obedient with a doom of falling fire that was swifter
than the thunderstone.

Maal Dweb had taken ever the fairest from among
the maidens of the planet Xiccarph; and no palace of
the walled towns, or savage outland cave, was exempt

from his unknown scrutiny. He had chosen no less than
fifty girls during the three decades of his tyranny; and
these, forsaking their lovers and kinsfolk voluntarily, lest
the wrath of Maal Dweb should descend upon them,
had gone one by one to the mountain citadel and were
lost behind its cryptic walls. There, as the odalisques of
the aging sorcerer, they were supposed to dwell in halls
that multiplied their beauty with a thousand mirrors;
and were said to have for servants women of brass and
men of iron that mimicked in all ways the motion and
speech of living people.

Tiglari had poured before Athle the uncouth adoration of his heart and the barbaric spoils of the chase, but
having many rivals, was still unsure of her favor. Cool as
a river-lily, and no less impartial, she had accepted his
worship and that of the others, among whom the warrior
Mocair was perhaps the most formidable. Returning at
eve from the hunt, Tiglari had found the tribe in lamen-
tation; and, learning that Athle had departed to the
harem of Maal Dweb, was swift to follow. He had not
announced his intention to his fellow tribesmen, since
the ears of Maal Dweb were everywhere; and he did not
know whether Mocair or any of the others had preceded
him in his desperate errantry. Mocair, however, had
been absent; and it was not unlikely that he had already
dared the obscure and hideous perils of the mountain.

The thought of this was enough to drive Tiglari forward with a rash disregard of the poisonous, reptile
flowers and clutching foliations. He came anon to a gap
in the horrible grove, and saw the saffron lights from the
lower windows of Maal Dweb, and a dark thronging of
domes and turrets that assailed the constellations above.
The lights were vigilant as the eyes of sleepless dragons,
and appeared to regard him with an evil, unblinking
awareness. But Tiglari leapt toward them, across the
gap, and heard the clash of sabered leaves that met behind him.

Before him was an open lawn, covered with a queer
grass that squirmed like innumerable worms beneath his
bare feet. He did not care to linger upon that lawn, but

ran onward with light, skimming paces. There were no footmarks in the grass; but nearing the portico of the palace, he saw a coil of thin rope that someone had flung aside, and knew that Mocair had preceded him.

There were paths of mottled marble about the palace, and fountains and waterfalls that played with a gurgling as of blood from the throats of carven monsters. The open portals were unguarded, and the whole building was still as a mausoleum lit by windless lamps. No shadows moved behind the brilliant yellow windows; and darkness slept unbroken among the high towers and cupolas. Tiglari, however, mistrusted sorely the appearance of quietude and slumber, and followed the bordering paths for some distance before daring to approach nearer to the palace.

Certain large and shadowy animals, which he took for the apish monsters of Maal Dweb, went by him in the gloom. They were hairy and uncouth, with sloping heads. Some of them ran in four-footed fashion, while others maintained the half-erect posture of anthropoids. They did not offer to molest Tiglari; but, whining dismally like dogs, they slunk away as if to avoid him. By this token, he knew that they were veritable beasts, and could not abide the odor with which he had smeared his limbs and torso.

At length, he came to a lampless portico with crowded columns. Here, with the silent gliding of a jungle snake, he entered the mysterious and ever-dreadful house of Maal Dweb. Behind the dark pillars, a door stood open; and beyond the door were the dim and seemingly endless reaches of an empty hall.

Tiglari went in with redoubled caution, and began to follow the arrased wall. The place was full of unknown perfumes, languorous and somnolent: a subtle reek as of censers in hidden alcoves of love. He did not like the perfumes; and the silence troubled him more and more as he went deeper into the palace. It seemed to him that the darkness was thick with unheard breathings, was alive with invisible and sinister movements.

Slowly, like the opening of great yellow eyes, the yel-

low flames arose in mighty lamps of copper that hung
along the hall. Tiglari hid himself behind a heavy-fig-
ured arras; but peeping out with eerie trepidation, he
saw that the hall was still deserted. Finally he dared to
resume his progress. All about him the imperial hangings, broidered with purple men and azure women on a
field of bright blood, appeared to stir with uneasy life
in a wind that he could not feel; and the lamps regarded
him with unwavering splendid eyes. But there was no
sign of the presence of Maal Dweb; and the metal servitors and human odalisques of the tyrant were nowhere
to be seen.

The doors on either side of the hall, with cunningly
mated valves of ebony and ivory, were all closed. At the
far end, Tiglari saw a rift of flaming light in a somber
double arras. Parting the arras very softly, he peered
into a huge, brilliantly illumined chamber that seemed
at first sight to be the harem of Maal Dweb, peopled
with all the girls that the enchanter had summoned to
his mountain dwelling over a course of decades. In fact,
it seemed that there were many hundrds, leaning or recumbent on ornate couches, or standing in attitudes of
languor or terror. Tiglari discerned in the throng the
women of Ommu-Zain, whose flesh is whiter than desert
salt; the slim girls of Uthmai, who are moulded from
breathing, palpitating jet; the queenly amber girls of
equatorial Xala; and the small women of Ilap, who have
the tones of newly greening bronze. But among them all,
he could not find the lillied beauty of Athle.

Greatly did he marvel at the number of the women
and the utter stillness with which they maintained their
various postures. There was no lifting nor falling of eyelids, no dropping of hands, no curving nor opening of
lips. They were like images of living, subtly painted
marble, or goddesses that slept in some enchanted hall
of eternity.

Tiglari, the intrepid hunter, was awed and frightened.
Here, surely, was proof of the fabled sorceries of Maal
Dweb. These women—if indeed they were women and
not mere statues—had been made the thralls of a death-

like spell of immortal slumber. It was as if some invisible medium of adamantine silence had filled the room, had formed about its occupants: a silence wherein, it seemed, no mortal being could draw breath.

However, if Tiglari were to continue his search for Maal Dweb and Athlé, it was necessary for him to traverse the enchanted chamber. Feeling that a marble sleep might descend upon him at the very crossing of the sill, he went in with holden breath and furtive pardlike paces. About him the women preserved their eternal stillness, their various airs and attitudes. Each, it appeared, had been overcome by the spell at the instant of some particular emotion, whether of fear, wonder, curiosity, vanity, weariness, anger or voluptuousness. Their number was fewer than he had supposed, and the room itself was smaller; but metal mirrors, panelling the walls, had created an illusion of multitude and immensity.

At the further end, he came to a second double arras, sightly parted, and revealing only shadow beyond. Peering through, he beheld a twilight chamber, illuminated dimly by two censers that gave forth a parti-colored glow and a red fume as of vaporing blood. The censers were set on lofty tripods in the far corners, facing each other. Between them, beneath a canopy of some dark and smouldering stuff with fringers braided like women's hair, was a couch of nocturnal purples with a valance of silver birds that fought against golden snakes. On the couch, in sober garments, a man reclined as if weary or asleep. The face of the man was a pale mask of mystery lying amid ambiguous shadows; but it did not occur to Tiglari that this being was any other than the redoubtable and tyrannic sorcerer whom he had come to slay. He knew that this was Maal Dweb, whom no man had seen in the flesh, but whose power was manifest to all; the occult, omniscient ruler of Xiccarph; the overlord of kings; the suzerain of the three suns and of all their moons and planets.

Like ghostly sentinels, the symbols of the grandeur of Maal Dweb, the images of his frightful empire, rose up to confront Tiglari. But the thought of Athle was a red mist that blotted all. He forgot his eerie terrors, his awe of that ensorcelled palace. The rage of the bereaved lover, the bloodthirst of the cunning hunter, awoke within him to guide his agile, stealthy paces, to make firm his powerful thews. The chamber was empty, except for the still and languid figure on the couch. Tiglari neared the unconscious sorcerer; and his hand grew tight on the hilt of the needle-like knife that was dipt in viper-venom.

The man before him lay with closed eyes and a cryptic weariness on his mouth and eyelids. He seemed to meditate rather than sleep, like one who wanders in a maze of distant memories or profound reveries. About him the walls were draped with funereal hangings, darkly and vaguely figured. Above him the twin censers wrought a cloudy glow, and diffused throughout the room their drowsy myrrh, which made the senses of Tiglari swim with a strange dimness.

Crouching tiger-wise beside the valance of birds and serpents, he made ready for the stroke. Then, mastering the subtle vertigo of the perfumes, he rose up; and his arm, with the darting movement of some heavy but supple adder, struck fiercely at the tyrant's heart.

It was as if he had tried to pierce a wall of adamant. In mid-air, before and above the recumbent enchanter, the knife clashed on some impenetrable substance that Tiglari could not see; and the point broke off and tinkled on the floor at his feet. Uncomprehending, baffled, he peered at the being whom he had sought to slay. Maal Dweb had not stirred nor opened his eyes. There was neither frown nor smile on his features; but their look of enigmatic weariness was somehow touched with a faint and cruel amusement.

Hesitantly, Tiglari put out his hand to verify a certain curious notion that had occurred to him. Even as he had suspected, there was no couch or canopy between the fuming censers—only a vertical, unbroken, highly-polished surface, in which the whole scene was apparently reflected. He had tried to kill a mirrored image. But, to his further mystification, he himself was not visible in the mirror.

He whirled about, thinking that Maal Dweb must be somewhere in the room. Even as he turned, the funereal draperies rushed back with an evil, silken whispering from the walls, as if drawn by unseen hands. The chamber leapt into sudden glaring light, the walls appeared to recede illimitably; and naked giants, whose umber-brown limbs and torsos glistened as if smeared with ointment, stood in menacing postures on every side. Their eyes glowered like those of jungle creatures; and each of them held an enormous knife, from which the point had been broken.

This, thought Tiglari, was a fearsome thaumaturgy; and he crouched down between the tripods, wary as a trapped animal, to await the assault of the giants. But these beings, crouching simultaneously, mimicked his every movement. By degrees it came to him that what he saw was his own reflection, multiplied and monstrously amplified in the mirrors of Maal Dweb.

He turned again. The tasseled canopy, the couch of night-dark purples with its figured valance, the reclining dreamer in plain vestments, all had vanished. Of that which he had beheld, only the smoking censers remained, rearing before a glassy wall that gave back like the others the reflection of Tiglari himself.

Bafflement and terror united now in the savage brain of the hunter. He felt that Maal Dweb, the all-seeing, all-potent magician, was playing a game and was deluding him with elaborate mockeries. Rashly indeed had Tiglari pitted his simple brawn and forest craft against a being of such supernatural power and demoniac artifice. He dared not stir; he scarcely ventured to breathe. The monstrous reflections appeared to watch him like ogres who guard a captive pygmy. The light, which emanated as if from hidden lamps in the mirrors, took on a more pitiless and alarming luster, and centered itself upon him with a silent horror. The vast, illusive reaches of the room appeared to deepen; and far away in their shadows, he saw the gathering of vapors with

human faces that melted and re-formed incessantly and
were never twice the same.

Ever the eerie radiance brightened; ever the mist of
faces, like a hell-born fume, dissolved and re-limned itself behind the immobile giants, in the lengthening vis-
tas. An unheard laughter, malevolent, scornful, seemed
to lurk beyond the stillness. How long Tiglari waited, he
could not tell; the bright and frozen horror of that room
was a thing apart from time.

Now, in the litten air, a voice began to speak: a voice
that was toneless, deliberate—and disembodied. It was
faintly contemptuous; a little weary; slightly cruel. It
was impossible to align or locate: near as the beating
of Tiglari's heart, and yet infinitely far.

"What do you seek, Tiglari?" said the voice. "Do you
think to enter with impunity the palace of Maal Dweb?
Others—many others, with the same intentions—have
come before you: but all have paid a certain price for
their temerity."

"I seek the maiden Athle," said Tiglari. "What have
you done with her?" The words were strange to him,
their very sound was remote, as if another than himself
had spoken.

"Athle is very beautiful," replied the voice. "It is the
will of Maal Dweb to make a certain use of her loveliness. The use is not one that should concern a hunter of
wild beasts . . . You are unwise, Tiglari."

"Where is Athle?" persisted the hunter.

"Athle has gone to find her fate in the labyrinth of
Maal Dweb. Not long ago, the warrior Mocair, who had
followed her to my palace, went out at my suggestion to
pursue his search amid the threadless windings of that
never to be exhausted maze. Go now, Tiglari, and seek
her also . . . There are many mysteries in my labyrinth;
and among them all, mayhap, there is one which you are
destined to solve."

The hunter saw that a door had opened in the mirror-
panelled wall. In the depth of the mirrors, two of the
metal slaves of Maal Dweb had appeared. Taller than
living men, and gleaming from head to foot with impla-

cable lusters as of burnished swords, they came forward upon Tiglari. The right arm of each was handed with a crescent sickle. Hastily, with no backward glance, the hunter went out through the open door. Behind him he heard the surly clash of its meeting valves.

The short night of the planet Xiccarph was not yet over; and the four moons had all gone down. But before him he saw the beginning of the fabled maze, illuminated clearly by glowing globular fruits that hung lantern-wise from baroque arches and arcades of foliage. Guided by their still, uncanny luminescence, he entered the labyrinth.

At first, it was a place of elfin fantasies and whims. There were quaintly-turned estrades, pillared with slim and antic trees, latticed with the drolly peering faces of extravagant orchids, that led the seeker to hidden, surprising bowers of goblinry. It was as if those outer meanderings had been planned merely to entice and bemuse and beguile.

Then, by vague degrees, as the hunter went on, it seemed that the designer's mood had darkened, had become more ominous and baleful. The trees that lined the path, with twisted, intertwinging boles, were Laocoons of struggle and torture, lit by enormous fungi that seemed to lift unholy tapers. The path itself ran downward, or climbed with evilly tilted steps through caverns of imbricated leafage that shone with the brazen glistening of dragon-scales. At every turning the way divided before Tiglari; the devious branchings multiplied; and skillful though he was in jungle-craft, it would have been wholly impossible for him to retrace his wanderings. He kept on, hoping that chance would somehow lead him to Athle; and many times he called her name aloud, but was answered only by remote, derisive echoes, or by the dolorous howling of some unseen beast that had become lost in the maze of Maal Dweb.

He came to eerie pools, alight with coiling and wreathing witch-fires, in dim arboreal grottoes. Greenish, bloated hands as of dead men appeared to lift from the changing films of phosphorescence; and once he thought that he beheld the drowning face of Athle. He plunged into the shallow pool—but found only fetid slime, and a swollen, nauseous thing that squirmed slowly beneath his touch.

Now he was mounting through arbors of malignant hydra growths that coiled and uncoiled about him tumultuously. The way lightened more and more; the night-shining fruits and blossoms were pale and sickly as the dying tapers of a witches' revel. The earliest of the three suns had risen; and its gamboge-yellow beams were filtering in through the plaited horrors of frilled and venomous vines.

Far off, and seeming to fall from some hidden height in the labyrinth before him, he heard a chorus of brazen voices that were like articulate bells or gongs. He could not distinguish the words; but the accents were those of a solemn and portentous announcement. They were fraught with mystic finality, with hieratic doom. They ceased; and there was no sound other than the hiss and rustle of swaying plants.

Tiglari went on. The tortuous maze became wilder and more anomalous. There were tiered growths, like obscene sculptures or architectural forms, that seemed to be of stone and metal. Others were like carnal nightmares of rooted flesh, that wallowed and fought and coupled in noisome ooze. Foul things with chancrous blossoms flaunted themselves on infernal obelisks. Living parasitic mosses of crimson crawled on vegetable monsters that swelled and bloated behind the columns of accursed pavilions.

It seemed now that the hunter's every step was predestined and dictated. He was no longer free to choose his way; for many of the paths were overgrown by things that he did not care to face; and others were blocked by horrid portcullises of cacti, or ended in pools whose waters teemed with leeches larger than tunnies. The second and third suns of Xiccarph arose; but their beams of emerald and carmine served but to heighten the terrors of the web that had closed in about Tiglari.

By stairs where floral serpents crept, and gradients

lined with tossing, clashing aloes, he climbed slowly on. Rarely could he see the labyrinthine reaches below, or the levels toward which he was tending. Somewhere on the blind path, he met one of the ape-like animals of Maal Dweb: a dark, savage creature, sleek and glistening like a wet otter, as if it had bathed in one of the hidden pools. It passed him with a hoarse growl, recoiling as the others had done from his repulsively smeared body . . . But nowhere could he find the maiden Athlé or the warrior Mocair, who had preceded him into the maze.

Now he had reached a curious little pavement of somber onyx, oblong, and wholly surrounded, except on the side of his approach, by enormous flowers with fluted bronze-like stems and great leaning balls that seemed to be the mottled heads of bestial chimeras, yawning to disclose their carmine throats. Through the gap in this singular hedge, he stepped forward on the pavement and stood staring irresolutely at the serried blooms: for here the way seemed to end.

The onyx beneath his feet was wet with some unknown, sticky fluid. He was dazed with the wonder, strangeness, and intricate, coiling horror through which he had passed; but a dim warning of peril stirred within him. He turned toward the gap through which he had entered, but his impulse of retreat was all too late. From the base of each of the tall flower stems, a long tendril like a wire of bronze uncoiled with lightning rapidity, and closed about his ankles. He stood trapped and helpless at the center of a taut net. Then, while he struggled ineffectually, the huge stems began to lean and tilt toward him, till the carmine mouths of the blossoms were close about his knees like a circle of fawning monsters.

Nearer they came, almost touching him. From their thick lips a clear, hueless liquid, dripping slowly at first, and then running in little rills, descended on his feet and ankles and shanks. Indescribably, his flesh crawled beneath it; then there was a peculiar, passing numbness; then a furious stinging like the bites of innumerable insects. Between the crowding heads of the flowers he saw that his legs had undergone a mysterious and horrifying change: their natural hairiness had thickened, had assumed a dark and shaggy pile like the fur of apes; the shanks themselves had somehow shortened; and the feet had grown longer, with uncouth finger-like toes such as were possessed by the animals of Maal Dweb!

In a frenzy of nameless alarm and fear, he drew his broken-tipped knife and began to slash at the flowers. It was as if he had struck at monstrous bells of ringing iron, had assailed the armored heads of dragons. The blade snapped at the hilt. Then the blossoms, lifting hideously, were leaning about his waist, were laving his hips and thighs in their thin, evil slaver.

Across the bizarre nightmare in which his brain and body were drowning impotently, he heard the startled cry of a woman. Through the open gap in the hedge, he beheld a strange scene which the hitherto impenetrable maze, parting as if by magic, had revealed. Fifty feet away, on the same level as the onyx pavement, there stood an elliptic dais or low altar of moonwhite stone at whose center the maiden Athle, emerging from the labyrinth on a raised walk of porphyry, had paused in an attitude of wonder. Before her, in the claws of an immense marble lizard that reared above the dais, a great circular mirror of steely metal was held upright, with the monster's head hidden from view behind it. Athle, as if fascinated by some celestial vision, was peering into the steely disk. She presented her wide-eyed profile to Tiglari; and the mirror itself was seen obliquely, with the foreshortened body of the lizard reaching away at a sharp angle and mingling obscenely with the half-retilian maze. Midway between the onyx pavement and the ellipse of pale stone, a row of six slender brazen columns, topped with graven heads like demoniac Termini, rose at broad intervals and faced alternately toward the hunter and the girl.

Tiglari would have called out to Athle; but at that moment she took a single step toward the mirror, as if drawn by something that she saw in its depths; and the dull disk seemed to brighten with some internal, incan-

descent flame. The eyes of the hunter were temporarily
blinded by the spiky rays that leapt forth from it for an
instant, enveloping and transfixing the maiden. When
the dimness cleared away in swirling blots of sultry
color, he saw that Athle, in a pose of statuesque rigidity,
was still regarding the mirror with startled eyes. She had
not moved; the wonder was frozen on her face: and it
came to Tiglari that she was like the women who slept
an enchanted slumber in the palace of Maal Dweb.
Even as this thought occurred to him, he heard a ringing
chorus of metallic voices, that seemed to emanate from
the graven demon heads upon the columns.

"The maiden Athle," announced the voices in solemn
and portentous tones, "has beheld herself in the mirror
of Eternity, and has passed forever beyond the changes
and corruptions of Time."

Tiglari felt that he was sinking into some enormous,
obscurely terrible fen of dreams. He could comprehend
nothing of what had befallen Athle; and his own fate
was an equally dark and dread enigma, beyond the solution of a simple hunter.

Now the leaning blossoms had lifted about his shoulders, were laving his arms, his body. Beneath their
abhorrent alchemy the transformation continued. A long
fur sprang up on the thickening torso; the arms length-
ened; they became simian; the hands took on a likeness
to the feet. From the neck downward, Tiglari differed in
no wise from the apes of the garden.

In helpless abject terror, he waited for the completion
of the metamorphosis. Then, slowly, he became aware
that a man in sober garments, with eyes and mouth re-
plete with the weariness of strange things, was standing
before him. Behind the man, as if attending him, were
two of the sickle-handed automatons of iron.

In a somewhat languid voice, the man uttered an unknown word that vibrated in the air with prolonged,
mysterious aftertones. The circle of craning flowers drew
back from Tiglari, resuming their former upright posi-
tions in a weird hedge; and the wiry tendrils were withdrawn from his ankles, leaving him free. Hardly able to

comprehend his release, he heard a sound of brazen voices, and knew dimly that the demon heads of the columns had spoken, saying:

"The hunter Tiglari has been laved in the nectar of the blossoms of primordial life, and has become in all ways, from the neck downward, even as the beasts that he hunted."

When the solemn chorus ceased, the weary man in sober raiment came nearer and addressed him:

"I, Maal Dweb, had intended to deal with you precisely as I dealt with Mocair and many others. Mocair was the beast that you met in the labyrinth, with new-made fur that was still sleek and wet from the liquor of the flowers; and you saw some of his predecessors about the palace. However, I find that my whims are not always the same. You, Tiglari, unlike the others, shall at least remain a man from the neck upward; and you are free to resume your wanderings in the labyrinth, and escape from it if you can. I do not wish to see you again, and my clemency arises from another reason than esteem for your kind. Go now: the maze has many windings which you are yet to traverse."

A dreadful awe was upon Tiglari; his native fierceness, his savage volition, were tamed by the enchanter's languid will. With one backward look of fearful concern and wonder at the frozen shape of Athle, he withdrew obediently, slouching like a huge ape. His fur glistening wetly to the three suns, he vanished amid the meanderings of the labyrinth.

Maal Dweb, attended by his metal slaves, went over to the figure of Athle, which still regarded the steely mirror with astonished eyes.

"Mong Lut," he said, addressing by name the nearer of the two automatons that followed at his heels, "it has been, as you know, my caprice to eternalize the frail beauty of women. Athle, like the others whom I have summoned to the mountain and have sent out to explore the ingenious secrets of my maze, has looked into that mirror whose sudden radiance turns the flesh to a stone that is fairer than marble and no less eternal . . . Also, as you know, it has been my whim to turn men into beasts with the copious fluid of certain artificial flowers, so that their outer semblance could conform strictly to their inner nature. Is it not well, Mong Lut, that I should have done these things? Am I not Maal Dweb, in whom all knowledge and all power reside?"

"Yes, master," echoed the automation in an iron voice, "you are Maal Dweb, the all-wise, the all-powerful, and it is well that you should have done these things."

"However," continued Maal Dweb, "the repetition of even the most remarkable thaumaturgies can grow monotonous after a certain number of times. I do not think that I shall deal again in this fashion with any woman, nor deal thus with any man. Is it not well, Mong Lut, that I should vary my sorceries in future. Am I not Maal Dweb, the all-resourceful?"

"Indeed, you are Maal Dweb," agreed the automation, "and it would be well for you to diversify your enchantments."

Maal Dweb, in his manner, was not ill pleased with the answers that the automation had given. He cared little for converse, other than the iron echoing of his metal servitors, who assented always to all that he said, and who spared him the tedium of arguments. And it may have been that there were times when he wearied a little even of this, and preferred the silence of the petrified women, or the muteness of the beasts that could no longer call themselves men.

Lin Carter

The Whelming Of Oom

❖⟡━⟡━⟡━⟡━⟡━⟡━⟡━⟡━⟡━⟡━⟡❖

THE INFLUENCE of Lord Dunsany on modern fantasy writers did not begin and end with members of the Lovecraft Circle, such as Clark Ashton Smith, Robert E. Howard, Robert Bloch (in the short tale "Black Lotus," at least, and H.P.L. himself.

Indeed, it still continues. My good friend and sometime collaborator L. Sprague de Camp admits to a powerful interest in Dunsany during his formative years, and I seem to see something in the fiction of Fritz Leiber, in Jack Vance and in the young British fantasy-writer Michael Moorcock which smacks of the Dunsanian.

To say nothing of myself.

For the past couple of years I have been quietly writing certain little tales laid in Simrana the Dreamworld, and these have, a couple of them, anyway, found their way into print. If you happen to have read one or another of them, the Dunsanian flavor should be unmistakable. At any rate, I unblushingly admit to the influence: Dunsany was one of the great masters of our craft, and few of us—least of all myself—have so fully mastered the techniques of fantasy writing that we could not still learn a thing or two from him.

For those who have not yet encountered my Simrana tales, let me give you a little information which may be relevant to your understanding of the tale. Simrana, I will have you know, is not one of your great, round, lumbering science fiction *planets*—to the contrary, it is the kind of world that should, but (sadly) does not, exist. Which is to say, Simrana is flat as a table-top, with fine square edges over which the unwary explorer can fall if he does not watch his steps with care; it boasts among its flora and fauna all the more interesting and amusing species which no longer seem to inhabit the more mundane of our zoology texts, such as the Su, the Basilisk, the Great Crimson Mantichore, the solitary Phoenix and the Dragon; magic in all its branches is a practical science quite widely studied in Simrana, while dreary sciences like geology, botany, astronomy and so on are shunned as verging on the occult and the nonsensical; and the place boasts a profusion of cities and realms all jumbled together with not the slightest regard for Historical Realism or Cultural Patterns. Moreover, and quite importantly, the Gods certainly exist in Simrana and play a very important role in the management of this newest of the Dreamworlds.

With these bits of information in mind, let us consider the tale . . . .

———————◆———————

T HEY SAY that once in Simrana the Dreamworld there dwelt in the Lands About Zuth in an idolatrous folk who turned from the Gods, saying: Let us fashion a God all our own, that we alone of all the nations may worship him.

Now there rose near Zuth a mighty mountain all of pure and perdurable emerald, stronger than granite, more lovely than marble. And looking upon it the folk said: Let us hew our God from this green stone, that he may tower above the works of men lesser than we.

So they set about their labor, to cut and carve the mountain into the likeness of the God they had invented, whom they had named by the name OOM for that there was no other God with that name known amongst the lands of men. And they did toil for generations in the fashioning of Oom, and little by little he emerged from the glistening emerald as they hacked and hewed, a finger here, there an eyebrow, a nostril, a curve of flank or cheek.

When that their toil was done, this was the likeness of Oom. The peak of the mountain was carven into his head whereon were four faces. The face that looked to the north was grim and foreboding of mien. The face toward the south was benign and smiling. The eastern face howled with a fury of rage. The face turned to the west was closed in sleep.

Eight arms had Oom, folded each two together against his chest.

He sat with his legs thus and so, in the manner of tailors, and in his lap they builded a city magnificent with gems and ivories and glittering marbles; a sacred city that was named On The Knees Of Oom. Then they were finished and could rest.

Now the Eight Hundred Gods Who Watch Over Simana care but little for the doings of men, despite what the priests will say. But that the folk who dwelt about Zuth turned from them to a God of their own devisal was an affront that they could not ignore. And they moved from their accustomed tranquility and were urged to wrath against this new God, Oom, and all they that worshipped him.

And the Highest Gods said to the least and littlest amongst them: Go up against Oom and throw him down, yea, and all those that call upon his name. For he is as a stench in Our nostrils and an abomination in Our sight; therefore whelm ye him and cast him down utterly in the dust.

And the Lesser Gods came unto those lands wherein Oom sat smiling upon the south, howling against the east, sternly glowering to the north, and dreaming at the west. And they unleashed against him the forces over which they had the mastering of, and these were the lesser powers of Nature.

SHAMMERING the Sunlight poured upon Oom the fierce blaze of noon, and THUTHOOL the Snow sheathed him in numb whiteness.

UMBALDROOM the Thunder smote him, and SHISH the Rain lashed his emerald flanks.

CHEEL, the God of Morning Dew, pearled him with chilly wetness. KAZANG the Lightning flickered about his crest. HASHOOVATH the Wind howled about his folded arms and tore at them with impalpable fingers.

Yet Oom sat unshaken and unchanged.

So it came to pass that the Seven Little Gods withdrew in defeat. But they say in Simrana that the Gods yield not before Necessity, and behold, they who were the Lesser raised a loud cry, beseeching the aid of Gods greater than they.

And the Greater Gods came unto Oom and set their forces up against him as the waves of Ocean go up against the bastions of the great cliffs that front the main.

GLAUN CHELID the Lord of Wintry Cold clasped his bitter cloak of glittering ice about Oom and froze him with that iron grip whereof the rocks are made to cry out and great trees are broke asunder.

RUZ THANNA the Lord of Summery Heat baked him in blasts of withering flame such as sear the burnt and cindery deserts of the ultimate south in scorching light of molten and fiery suns.

THOOZ LASHLAR the Lord of Mighty Rains hurled against Oom his raging torrents from full-bellied clouds, in roaring floods such as drown kingdoms and wash cities to rubble and feed rivers into gorged and swollen monsters that ravish the earth.

VOSHT THONDAZOOR the Lord of the Tempest set upon Oom his savage servants, the raging Thunderstorm, the ferocious Whirlwind, the screaming Hurricane, and all the legions of the nine and ninety Winds.

But naught availeth against Oom.

In their desperation, the Greater Gods roused even their dread and terrible brother, yea, even SKAGANAK BELBADOOM the Earthquake, from his surly and ominous slumbers in the deeps of the clefts of the earth. And he came and shook Oom with all his thunders such as make the very hills to tremble, but he whelmed him not.

Then came forward one whose shadowy face was hidden and whose voice was low and monotonous, who spake softly, saying: I will whelm Oom, even I, TA-TOKTA the Lord of Passing Moments.

And they laughed and mocked him, for Time is the least and smallest servant of the Gods.

But he set upon Oom the measureless passing moments, whereof are builded the millions of years. And each small moment, as it went past, bore away from Oom one single grain of dust.

And, lo! Oom crumbled. Before the assault of Time his vast four-featured visage wore smooth until he frowned no longer, neither did he smile, nor howl, nor dream no more.

His limbs fell from him as dust falls, grain by impalpable grain. His massive and perdurable torso eroded and even his knees whereon was builded The City Sacred To Oom, they were no more, and the city itself was but scattering dust. And the people thereof fled by night, saying: Oom is fallen, Oom is overthrown, let us call no longer upon Oom, for behold the Gods are stronger than he.

And Oom was not. In his place stretched away a barren and desolate desert. And the sands of this desert were green as the powdery dust of emeralds.

And the Eight Hundred Gods rejoiced and trooped in all their glory and gorgeousness past their grey servant Time to their tall thrones amidst the stars. And the eyes of Tatokta moved a little sidewise as if measuring their thrones, the splendour and the might thereof, and he said softly to himself: These, too, I shall whelm with my aeons. But not yet. Not yet . . .

So they tell the tale in Simrana.

A. Merritt

Through The Dragon Glass

❖ ❀══❀══❀══❀══❀══❀══❀══❀══❀══❀══❀ ❖

NEITHER James Branch Cabell nor H. P. Lovecraft has matched the magnificent popularity of yet a third American master of fantastic literature, the great A. Merritt.

Abraham Merritt was born in Bemerly, New Jersey, on January 20, 1884—two years after E. R. Eddison and five years after Cabell. Like Clark Ashton Smith, Merritt was largely a self-educated man. He managed to complete the first year of high school, but that was enough for him. Still a teen-aged boy, he left home to go treasure-hunting among the ruined cities of jungled Yucatan, and became one of the first white men in a hundred years to enter the ancient Mayan city of Tuluum (which sounds just like a beginning for one of his own novels).

His was an extraordinary life, and he was an unusual man with many strange and curious interests. He was as deeply learned in the shadowy mazes of obscure Oriental mythologies as many college professors; he was passionately interested in subtropical horticulture, and filled his home with exotic, rare and poisonous plants; he was also an expert apiarist (a ten-dollar word which means he bred and raised bees); he was perhaps the most popular adventure-story writer of his day, and also one of the greatest newspaper editors in America.

Newspaper publishing was his lifelong career. At 18 he became a reporter for the *Philadelphia Inquirer*, covering murders, hangings, suicides and many unsolved

126

mysteries; by 24 he was night editor, and at 37 he became editor-in-chief of William Randolph Hearst's great publication *The American Weekly*, one of the most influential newspaper posts in the entire country, and a position he held for many years. He died in 1943 of a heart attack. He was only 59.

Although his editorial tasks were very demanding and consumed much of his time and energy, he found enough leisure to write a small quantity of imaginative fiction, nine novels and a total of six short stories. As well, there were found among his papers after his death four unfinished fragments, two of which were completed by the fantasy artist Hannes Bok and published under the titles of *The Fox Woman* and *The Black Wheel*.

Merritt's novels derive almost entirely from the sort of "lost race" story made popular by Sir Henry Rider Haggard (1856–1925). You know what I mean—the sort of story wherein an explorer from the modern world outside penetrates the jungled depths of unknown Africa or the snowy Himalayas, and finds a long-lost colony of ancient Phoenicians or Romans or Egyptians or something, still going strong after all those centuries. Haggard did not exactly invent this kind of yarn, but he was far and away the most successful writer to try his hand at the genre. With two novels, published consecutively and only a year apart (*King Solomon's Mines*, 1886, and the immortal *She* in 1887), he became sensationally famous and both of those two early books have remained in print to this very day.

Almost every other writer in England tried "doing a Haggard," as it was called: Conan Doyle in *The Lost World*, and Rudyard Kipling, a lifelong friend of Haggard's who sometimes collaborated with him on plotting his novels, and many another writer, including Edgar Rice Burroughs (remember all those Tarzan novels wherein the Lord of the Jungle finds a lost colony of Rome, Egypt or Atlantis?).

A. Merritt published the first part of his famous novel *The Moon Pool* in *All-Story Weekly*, June 22, 1918. It was an immediate sensation, demanding a sequel which began appearing nine months later, and went into hardcover book form from Putnam's in 1919. In one form or another, the two parts have since been reprinted in the United States alone at least eighteen times.

The success of *The Moon Pool* was more than equalled by the publication of *The Face in the Abyss* in 1923, and thereafter appeared novel after novel until Merritt's death. His stories have been translated into French, Spanish, Dutch and Russian, and published in at least nine countries. Hollywood has filmed two of his novels: *Seven Footprints to Satan* in 1929 and *Burn Witch Burn* in 1936, with Lionel Barrymore, Maureen O'Sullivan and Erich von Stroheim. In the Avon paperback editions alone, over five million copies of his novels have been sold.

Merritt's influence has been considerable, and it continues. Henry Kuttner's *The Dark World,* and several of his other magazine novels, are excellent imitations of Merrittesque romance; most of the "lost race" novels published since Merritt's day show unmistakable signs of his influence; and late this year, The Ballantine Adult Fantasy Series will present the first paperback edition of a thrilling fantasy novel by the artist Hannes Bok called *Sorcerer's Ship.* Bok was Merritt's most devoted disciple —as a boy he once copied out the whole of *The Ship of Ishtar* in longhand because he had to return the copies of *Argosy All-Story* which he had borrowed in order to read the serial—and, although *Sorcerer's Ship* is quite original in form and concept, it is colored throughout by Hannes Bok's enthusiasm for Merritt and I strongly doubt if he would ever have written his novel without the example of *Ishtar* to hand.

*

I suppose the "lost race" yarn must be considered a sub-branch or a related genre to the imaginary world story, although I am not completely satisfied with the relationship. However, and happily, Merritt wrote at least one tale which is completely in the Morris/Dunsany/Eddison tradition of the invented world. I reproduce it here in its first reprinting in many years.

Merritt originally wrote this story over half a century ago: it first appeared in *All-Story Weekly,* the issue of November 24, 1917. It came out, then, a good seven months

before the opening of *The Moon Pool*. It was the first piece
of fiction ever published under the name of A. Merritt: it
remains to this day one of the most gripping and imaginative . . . .

———◆———

Herndon helped loot the Forbidden City when the
Allies turned the suppression of the Boxers into the most
gorgeous burglar-party since the days of Tamerlane. Six
of his sailormen followed faithfully his buccaneering
fancy. A sympathetic Russian highness whom he had en-
tertained in New York saw to it that he got to the coast
and his yacht. That is why Herndon was able to sail
through the Narrows with as much of the Son of Heav-
en's treasures as the most accomplished laborer in Peking's mission vineyard.

Some of the loot he gave to charming ladies who had
dwelt or were still dwelling on the sunny side of his
heart. Most of it he used to fit up those two astonishing
Chinese rooms in his Fifth Avenue house. And a little of
it, following a vague religious impulse, he presented to
the Metropolitan Museum. This, somehow, seemed to
put the stamp of legitimacy on his part of the pillage—
like offerings to the gods and building hospitals and
peace palaces and such things.

But the Dragon Glass, because he had never seen anything quite so wonderful, he set up in his bedroom
where he could look at it the first thing in the morning,
and he placed shaded lights about it so that he could
wake up in the night and look at it! Wonderful? It is
more than wonderful, the Dragon Glass! Whoever made
it lived when the gods walked about the earth creating
something new every day. Only a man who lived in that
sort of atmosphere could have wrought it. There was
never anything like it.

I was in Hawaii when the cables told of Herndon's

first disappearance. There wasn't much to tell. This man had gone to his room to awaken him one morning—and Herndon wasn't there. All his clothes were, though. Everything was just as if Herndon ought to be somewhere in the house—only he wasn't.

A man worth ten millions can't step out into thin air and vanish without leaving behind him the probability of some commotion, naturally. The newspapers attended to the commotion, but the columns of type boiled down to essentials contained just two facts—that Herndon had come home the night before, and in the morning he was undiscoverable.

I was on the high seas, homeward bound to help in the search, when the wireless told the story of his reappearance. They had found him on the floor of his bedroom, shreds of a silken robe on him, and his body mauled as though by a tiger. But there was no more explanation of his return than there had been of his disappearance.

The night before he hadn't been there—and in the morning there he was. Herndon, when he was able to talk, utterly refused to confide in his doctors. I went straight through to New York, and waited until the men of medicine decided that it was better to let him see me than to have him worry any longer about not seeing me.

Herndon got up from a big invalid chair when I entered. His eyes were clear and bright, and there was no weakness in the way he greeted me, nor in the grip of his hand. A nurse slipped from the room.

"What was it, Jim?" I cried. "What on earth happened to you?"

"Not so sure it was on earth," he said. He pointed to what looked like a tall easel hooded with a heavy piece of silk covered with embroidered Chinese characters. He hesitated for a moment and then walked over to the closet. He drew out two heavy bore guns, the very ones, I remembered, that he had used in his last elephant hunt.

"You won't think me crazy if I ask you to keep one of these handy while I talk, will you, Ward?" he asked rather apologetically. "This looks pretty real, doesn't it?"

He opened his dressing gown and showed me his chest swathed in bandages. He gripped my shoulder as I took without question one of the guns. He walked to the easel and drew off the hood.

"There it is," said Herndon.

And then, for the first time, I saw the Dragon Glass!

There has never been anything like that thing! Never! At first all you saw was a cool, green, glimmering translucence, like the sea when you are swimming under water on a still summer day and look up through it. Around its edges ran flickers of scarlet and gold, flashes of emerald, shimmers of silver and ivory. At its base a disk of topaz rimmed with red fire shot up dusky little vaporous yellow flames.

Afterward you were aware that the green translucence was an oval slice of polished stones. The flashes and flickers became dragons. There were twelve of them. Their eyes were emeralds, their fangs were ivory, their claws were gold. There were scaled dragons and each scale was so inlaid that the base, green as the primeval jungle, shaded off into a vivid scarlet, and the scarlet into tips of gold. Their wings were of silver and vermilion, and were folded close to their bodies.

But they were alive, those dragons. There was never so much life in metal and wood since Al-Akram, the sculptor of ancient Ad, carved the first crocodile, and the jealous Almighty breathed life into it for a punishment!

And last you saw that the topaz disk that sent up little yellow flames was the top of a metal sphere around which coiled a thirteenth dragon, thin and red, and biting its scorpion-tipped tail.

It took your breath away, the first glimpse of the Dragon Glass. Yes, and the second and third glimpse, too—and every other time you looked at it.

"Where did you get it?" I asked, a little shakily.

Herndon said evenly: "It was in a small hidden crypt in the Imperial Palace. We broke into the crypt quite by"—he hesitated—"well, call it by accident. As soon as I saw it I knew I must have it. What do you think of it?"

"Think!" I cried. "Think! Why, it's the most marvelous thing that the hands of man ever made! What is that stone? Jade?"

"I'm not sure," said Herndon. "But come here. Stand just in front of me."

He switched out the lights in the room. He turned another switch, and on the glass opposite me three shaded electrics threw their rays into its mirror-like oval.

"Watch!" said Herndon. "Tell me what you see!"

I looked into the glass. At first I could see nothing but the rays shining farther, farther—into infinite distances, it seemed. And then—

"Good God!" I cried, stiffening with horror. "Jim, what hellish thing is this?"

"Steady, old man," came Herndon's voice. There was relief and a curious sort of joy in it. "Steady; tell me just what you see."

I said: "I seem to see through infinite distances—and yet what I see is as close to me as though it were just on the other side of the glass. I see a cleft that cuts through two masses of darker green. I see a claw, a gigantic, hideous claw that stretches out through the cleft. The claw has seven talons that open and close—open and close. Good God, such a claw, Jim! It is like the claws that reach out from the holes in the lama's hell to grip the blind souls as they shudder by!"

"Look, look farther, up through the cleft, above the claw. It widens. What do you see?"

I said: "I see a peak rising enormously high and cutting the sky like a pyramid. There are flashes of flame that dart from behind and outline it. I see a great globe of light like a moon that moves slowly out of the flashes: there is another moving across the breast of the peak; there is a third that swims into the flame at the farthest edge—"

"The seven moons of Rak," whispered Herndon, as though to himself. "The seven moons that bathe in the rose flames of Rak which are the fires of life and that circle Lalil like a diadem. He upon whom the seven moons of Rak have shown is bound to Lalil for this life, and for ten thousand lives."

He reached over and turned the switch again. The lights of the room sprang up.

"Jim," I said, "it can't be real! What is it? Some devil-'sh illusion in the glass?"

He unfastened the bandages about his chest.

"The claw you saw had seven talons," he answered quietly. "Well, look at this."

Across the white flesh of his breast, from left shoulder to the lower ribs on the right, ran seven healing furrows. They looked as though they had been made by a gigantic steel comb that had been drawn across him. They ~ave one the thought they had been plowed.

"The claw made these," he said as quietly as before.

"Ward," he went on, before I could speak, "I wanted you to see—what you've seen. I didn't know whether you would see it. I don't know whether you'll believe me even now. I don't suppose I would if I were in your place—still—"

He walked over and threw the hood upon the Dragon Glass.

"I'm going to tell you," he said. "I'd like to go through it—uninterrupted. That's why I cover it.

"I don't suppose," he began slowly—"I don't suppose, Ward, that you've ever heard of Rak the Wonder-Worker, who lived somewhere back at the beginning of things, nor how the Greatest Wonder-Worker banished him somewhere outside the world?"

"No," I said shortly, still shaken by what I had seen.

"It's a big part of what I've got to tell you," he went on. "Of course you'll think it rot, but—I came across the legend in Tibet first. Then I ran across it again—with the names changed, of course—when I was getting away from China.

"I take it that the gods were still fussing around close to man when Rak was born. The story of his parentage is somewhat scandalous. When he grew older, Rak wasn't satisfied with just seeing wonderful things being done. He wanted to do them himself, and he—well, he studied the method. After a while the Greatest Wonder-Worker ran across some of the things Rak had made, and he found them admirable—a little too admirable. He didn't like to destroy the lesser wonder-worker because, so the gossip ran, he felt a sort of responsibility. So he gave Rak a place somewhere—outside the world—and he gave him power over every one out of so many millions of births to lead or lure or sweep that soul into his domain so that he might build up a people—and over his people Rak was given the high, the low, and the middle justice.

"And outside the world Rak went. He fenced his domain about with clouds. He raised a great mountain, and on its flank he built a city for the men and women who were to be his. He circled the city with wonderful gardens, and he placed in the gardens many things, some good and some very—terrible. He set around the mountain's brow seven moons for a diadem, and he fanned behind the mountain a fire which is the fire of life, and through which the moons pass eternally to be born again."

Herndon's voice sank to a whisper.

"Through which the moons pass," he said. "And with them the souls of the people of Rak. They pass through the fires and are born again—and again—for ten thousand lives. I have seen the moons of Rak and the souls that march with them into the fires. There is no sun in the land—only the new-born moons that shine green on the city and on the gardens."

"Jim," I cried impatiently. "What in the world are you talking about? Wake up, man! What's all that nonsense got to do with this?"

I pointed to the hooded Dragon Glass.

"That," he said. "Why, through that lies the road to the gardens of Rak!"

The heavy gun dropped from my hand as I stared at him, and from him to the glass and back again. He smiled and pointed to his bandaged breast.

He said: "I went straight through to Peking with the Allies. I had an idea what was coming, and I wanted to be in at the death. I was among the first to enter the Forbidden City. I was as mad for loot as any of them. It was a maddening sight, Ward. Soldiers with their arms full of precious stuff even Morgan couldn't buy; soldiers with wonderful necklaces around their hairy throats and their pockets stuffed with jewels; soldiers with their shirts bulging treasures the Sons of Heaven had been hoarding for centuries! We were Goths sacking imperial Rome. Alexander's hosts pillaging that ancient gemmed courtezan of cities, royal Tyre! Thieves in the great ancient scale, a scale so great that it raised even thievery up to something heroic.

"We reached the throne-room. There was a little passage leading off to the left, and my men and I took it. We came into a small octagonal room. There was nothing in it except a very extraordinary squatting figure of jade. It squatted on the floor, its back turned toward us. One of my men stooped to pick it up. He slipped. The figure flew from his hand and smashed into the wall. A slab swung outward. By a—well, call it a fluke, we had struck the secret of the little octagonal room!

"I shoved a light through the aperture. It showed a crypt shaped like a cylinder. The circle of the floor was about ten feet in diameter. The walls were covered with paintings, Chinese characters, queer-looking animals, and things I can't well describe. Around the room, about seven feet up, ran a picture. It showed a sort of island floating off into space. The clouds lapped its edges like frozen seas full of rainbows. There was a big pyramid of a mountain rising out of the side of it. Around its peak were seven moons, and over the peak—a face!

"I couldn't place that face and I couldn't take my eyes off it. It wasn't Chinese, and it wasn't of any other race I'd ever seen. It was as old as the world and as young as tomorrow. It was benevolent and malicious, cruel and kindly, merciful and merciless, saturnine as Satan and as joyous as Apollo. The eyes were as yellow as buttercups, or as the sunstone on the crest of the Feathered Serpent they worship down in the Hidden Temple of Tuloon. And they were as wise as Fate.

"'There's something else here, sir,' said Martin—you remember Martin, my first officer. He pointed to a shrouded thing on the side. I entered, and took from the thing a covering that fitted over it like a hood. It was the Dragon Glass!

"The moment I saw it I knew I had to have it—and I knew I would have it. I felt I did not want to get the thing away any more than the thing itself wanted to get away. From the first I thought of the Dragon Glass as something alive. Just as much alive as you and I are. Well, I did get it away. I got it down to the yacht, and then the first odd thing happened.

"You remember Wu-Sing, my boat steward? You know the English Wu-Sing talks. Atrocious! I had the Dragon Glass in my stateroom. I'd forgotten to lock the door. I heard a whistle of sharply indrawn breath. I turned, and there was Wu-Sing. Now, you know that Wu-Sing isn't what you'd call intelligent-looking. Yet as he stood there something seemed to pass over his face, and very subtly change it. The stupidity was wiped out as though a sponge had been passed over it. He did not raise his eyes, but he said, in perfect English, mind you: 'Has the master augustly counted the cost of his possession?'

"I simply gaped at him.

"'Perhaps,' he continued, 'the master has never heard of the illustrious Hao-Tzan? Well, he shall hear.'

"Ward, I couldn't move or speak. But I know now it wasn't sheer astonishment that held me. I listened while Wu-Sing went on to tell in polished phrases the same story that I had heard in Tibet, only there they called him Rak instead of Hao-Tzan. But it was the same story.

"'And,' he finished, 'before he journeyed afar, the illustrious Hao-Tzan caused a great marvel to be wrought. He called it the Gateway!' Wu-Sing waved his hand at the Dragon Glass. 'The master has it. But what shall he who has a Gateway do but pass through it? Is it not better to leave the Gateway behind—unless he dare go through it?'

"He was silent. I was silent, too. All I could do was

wonder where the fellow had so suddenly got his command of English. And then Wu-Sing straightened. For a moment his eyes looked into mine. They were as yellow as buttercups, Ward, and wise, wise! My mind rushed back to the little room behind the panel. Ward—the eyes of Wu-Sing were the eyes of the face that brooded over the peak of the seven moons!

"And all in a moment, the face of Wu-Sing dropped back into its old familiar stupid lines. The eyes he turned to me were black and clouded. I jumped from my chair.

"'What do you mean, you yellow fraud!' I shouted. 'What do you mean by pretending all this time that you couldn't talk English?'

"He looked at me stupidly, as usual. He whined in his pidgin that he didn't understand; that he hadn't spoken a word to me until then. I couldn't get anything else out of him, although I nearly frightened his wits out. I had to believe him. Besides, I had seen his eyes. Well, I was fair curious by this time, and I was more anxious to get the glass home safely than ever.

"I got it home. I set it up here, and I fixed those lights as you saw them. I had a sort of feeling that the glass was waiting—for something. I couldn't tell just what. But that it was going to be rather important, I knew—"

He suddenly thrust his head into his hands, and rocked to and fro.

"How long, how long," he moaned, "how long, Santhu?"

"Jim!" I cried. "Jim! What's the matter with you?"

He straightened. "In a moment you'll understand," he said.

And then, as quietly as before: "I felt that the glass was waiting. The night I disappeared I couldn't sleep. I turned out the lights in the room; turned them on around the glass and sat before it. I don't know how long I sat but all at once I jumped to my feet. The dragons seemed to be moving! They were moving! They were crawling round and round the glass. They moved faster and faster. The thirteenth dragon spun about the topaz globe. They circled faster and faster until they were nothing but a halo of crimson and gold flashes. As they spun, the glass itself grew misty, mistier, mistier still, until it was nothing but a green haze. I stepped over to touch it. My hand went straight on through it as though nothing were there.

"I reached in—up to the elbow, up to the shoulder. I felt my hand grasped by warm little fingers. I stepped through—"

"Stepped through the glass?" I cried.

"Through it," he said, "and then—I felt another little hand touch my face. I saw Santhu!

"Her eyes were as blue as the corn flowers, as blue as the big sapphire that shines in the forehead of Vishnu, in his temple at Benares. And they were set wide, wide apart. Her hair was blue-black, and fell in two long braids between her little breasts. A golden dragon crowned her, and through its paws slipped the braids. Another golden dragon girded her. She laughed into my eyes, and drew my head down until my lips touched hers. She was lithe and slender and yielding as the reeds that grow before the Shrine of Hathor that stands on the edge of the Pool of Djeeba. Who Santhu is, or where she came from—how do I know? But this I know—she is lovelier than any woman who ever lived on earth. And she is a woman!

"Her arms slipped from about my neck and she drew me forward. I looked about me. We stood in a cleft between two great rocks. The rocks were a soft green, like the green of the Dragon Glass. Behind us was a green mistiness. Before us the cleft ran only a little distance. Through it I saw an enormous peak jutting up like a pyramid, high, high into a sky of chrysopase. A soft rose radiance pulsed at its sides, and swimming slowly over its breast was a huge globe of green fire. The girl pulled me gently toward the opening. We walked on silently, hand in hand. Quickly it came to me—Ward, I was in the place whose pictures had been painted in the room of the Dragon Glass!

"We came out of the cleft and into a garden. The Gardens of Many-Columned Iram, lost in the desert because they were too beautiful, must have been like that place. There were strange, immense trees whose branches were like feathery plumes and whose plumes shone with fires like those that clothe the feet of Indra's dancers. Strange flowers raised themselves along our path, and their hearts glowed like the glow-worms that are fastened to the rainbow bridge to Asgard. A wind sighed through the plumed trees, and luminous shadows drifted past their trunks. I heard a girl laugh, and the voice of a man singing.

"We went on. Once there was a low wailing far in the garden, and the girl threw herself before me, her arms outstretched. The wailing ceased, and we went on. The mountain grew plainer. I saw another globe of green fire swing out of the rose flashes at the right of the peak. I saw another shining into the glow at the left. There was a curious trail of mist behind it. It was a mist that had tangled in it a multitude of little stars. Everything was bathed in a soft green light—such a light as you would have if you lived within a pale emerald.

"We turned and went along another little trail. The little trail ran up a little hill, and on the hill was a little house. It looked as though it was made of ivory. It was a very odd little house. It was more like the Jain pagodas at Brahmaputra than anything else. The walls glowed as though they were full of light. The girl touched the wall, and a panel slid away. We entered, and the panel closed after us.

"The room was filled with a whispering yellow light. I say whispering because that is how one felt about it. It was gentle and alive. A stairway of ivory ran up to another room above. The girl pressed me toward it. Neither of us had uttered a word. There was a spell of silence upon me. I could not speak. There seemed to be nothing to say. I felt a great rest and a great peace—as though I had come home. I walked up the stairway and into the room above. It was dark except for a bar of green light that came through the long and narrow window. Through it I saw the mountain and its moons. On the floor was an ivory head-rest and some silken cloths. I felt suddenly very sleepy. I dropped to the cloths, and at once was asleep.

"When I awoke the girl with the corn-flower eyes was beside me! She was sleeping. As I watched, her eyes opened. She smiled and drew me to her—

"I do not know why, but a name came to me. 'Santhu!' I cried. She smiled again, and I knew that I had called her name. It seemed to me that I remembered her, too, out of immeasurable ages. I arose and walked to the window. I looked toward the mountain. There were now two moons on its breast. And then I saw the city that lay on the mountain's flank. It was such a city as you see in dreams, or as the tale-tellers of El-Bahara fashion out of the mirage. It was all of ivory and shining greens and flashing blues and crimsons. I could see people walking about its streets. There came the sound of little golden bells chiming.

"I turned toward the girl. She was sitting up, her hands clasped about her knees, watching me. Love came, swift and compelling. She arose—I took her in my arms—

"Many times the moons circled the mountain, and the mist held the little tangled stars passing with them. I saw no one but Santhu; no thing came near us. The trees fed us with fruits that had in them the very essence of life. Yes, the fruit of the Tree of Life that stood in Eden must have been like the fruit of those trees. We drank of green water that sparkled with green fires, and tasted like the wine Osiris gives the hungry souls in Amenti to strengthen them. We bathed in pools of carved stone that welled with water yellow as amber. Mostly we wandered in the gardens. There were many wonderful things in the gardens. They were very unearthly. There was no day or night. Only the green glow of the ever-circling moons. We never talked to each other. I don't know why. Always there seemed nothing to say.

"Then Santhu began to sing to me. Her songs were strange songs. I could not tell what the words were. But they built up pictures in my brain. I saw Rak the Wonder-Worker fashioning his gardens, and filling them with things beautiful and things—evil. I saw him raise the peak, and knew that it was Lalil; saw him fashion the seven moons and kindle the fires that are the fires of life. I saw him build his city, and I saw men and women pass into it from the world through many gateways.

"Santhu sang—and I knew that the marching stars in the mist were the souls of the people of Rak which sought rebirth. She sang, and I saw myself ages past walking in the city of Rak with Santhu beside me. Her song wailed, and I felt myself one of the mist-entangled stars. Her song wept, and I felt myself a star that fought against the mist, and, fighting, break away—a star that fled out and out through immeasurable green space—

"A man stood before us. He was very tall. His face was both cruel and kind, saturnine as Satan and joyous as Apollo. He raised his eyes to us, and they were yellow as buttercups, and wise, so wise! Ward, it was the face above the peak in the room of the Dragon Glass! The eyes that had looked at me out of Wu-Sing's face! He smiled on us for a moment and then—he was gone!

"I took Santhu by the hand and began to run. Quite suddenly it came to me that I had enough of the haunted gardens of Rak; that I wanted to get back to my own land. But not without Santhu. I tried to remember the road to the cleft. I felt that there lay the path back. We ran. From far behind came a wailing. Santhu screamed—but I knew the fear in her cry was not for herself. It was for me. None of the creatures of that place could harm her who was herself one of its creatures. The wailing drew closer. I turned.

"Winging down through the green air was a beast, an unthinkable beast, Ward! It was like the winged beast of the Apocalypse that is to bear the woman arrayed in purple and scarlet. It was beautiful even in its horror. It closed its scarlet and golden wings, and its long gleaming body shot at me like a monstrous spear.

"And then—just as it was about to strike—a mist threw itself between us! It was a rainbow mist, and it was—

cast. It was cast as though a hand had held it and thrown it like a net. I heard the winged beast shriek its disappointment. Santhu's hand gripped mine tighter. We ran through the mist.

"Before us was the cleft between the two green rocks. Time and time again we raced for it, and time and time again that beautiful shining horror struck at me—and each time came the thrown mist to baffle it. It was a game! Once I heard a laugh, and then I knew who was my hunter. The master of the beast and the caster of the mist. It was he of the yellow eyes—and he was playing me —playing me as a child plays with a cat when he tempts it with a piece of meat and snatches the meat away again and again from the hungry jaws!

"The mist cleared away from its last throw, and the mouth of the cleft was just before us. Once more the thing swooped—and this time there was no mist. The player had tired of the game! As it struck, Santhu raised herself before it. The beast swerved—and the claw that had been stretched to rip me from throat to waist struck me a glancing blow. I fell—fell through leagues and leagues of green space.

"When I awoke I was here in this bed with the doctor men around me and this—" He pointed to his bandaged breast again.

"That night when the nurse was asleep I got up and looked into the Dragon Glass, and I saw—the claw, even as you did. The beast is there. It is waiting for me!"

Herndon was silent for a moment.

"If he tires of the waiting he may send the beast through for me," he said. "I mean the man with the yellow eyes. I've a desire to try one of these guns on it. It's real, you know, the beast is—and these guns have stopped elephants."

"But the man with the yellow eyes, Jim," I whispered —"who is he?"

"He," said Herndon—"why, he's the Wonder-Worker himself!"

"You don't believe such a story as that!" I cried. "Why, it's—it's lunacy! It's some devilish illusion in the glass. It's like the—the crystal globe that makes you hypnotize yourself and think the things your own mind creates are real. Break it, Jim! It's devilish! Break it!"

"Break it!" he said incredulously. "Break it? Not for the ten thousand lives that are the toll of Rak! Not real? Aren't these wounds real? Wasn't Santhu real? Break it! Good God, man, you don't know what you say! Why, it's my only road back to her! If that yellow-eyed devil back there were only as wise as he looks, he would know he didn't have to keep his beast watching there. I want to go, Ward; I want to go and bring her back with me. I've an idea somehow, that he hasn't—well, full control of things. I've an idea that the Greatest Wonder-Worker wouldn't put wholly in Rak's hands the souls that wander through the many gateways into his kingdom. There's a way out, Ward; there's a way to escape him. I won away from him once, Ward. I'm sure of it. But then I left Santhu behind. I have to go back for her. That's why I found the little passage that led from the throne-room. And he knows it, too. That's why he had to turn his beast on me.

"And I'll go through again, Ward. And I'll come back again—with Santhu!"

*

But he has not returned. It is six months now since he disappeared for the second time. And from his bedroom, as he had done before. By the will that they found—the will that commanded that in the event of his disappearing as he had done before and not returning within a week, I was to have his house and all that was within it —I came into possession of the Dragon Glass. The dragons had spun again for Herndon, and he had gone through the gateway once more. I found only one of the elephant guns, and I knew that he had had time to take the other with him.

I sit night after night before the glass, waiting for him to come back through it—with Santhu. Sooner or later they will come. That I know.

Robert E. Howard

The Valley Of The Worm

ONE OF THE most remarkable careers in modern fantasy
fiction ended at eight o'clock on the hot summer morning
of July 11, 1936, when Robert E. Howard put a pistol to
his head and blew his brains out.

Howard was just 30 when he died. He was born in
1906 in the town of Peaster, Texas. He spent most of his
life in another Texas town called Cross Plains, some for-
ty-three miles southeast of Abilene.

Precocious, brilliant and rather frail, Howard spent a
lonely boyhood. Bullied by healthier children, he turned
to books for companionship and became a voracious
reader of pulp adventure writers like Edgar Rice Burroughs, Talbot Mundy, Harold Lamb, and of Robert W.
Chambers' novels of Indian warfare in Colonial upstate
New York. When he was about 17, the great *Weird
Tales* began publishing. Howard sold his first stories
while still in his teens. He was what we call a "born story-teller," and before long he joined that talented company of gifted fantasy writers that made *Weird Tales*
great—writers like H. P. Lovecraft, Clark Ashton Smith,
Robert Bloch and E. Hoffman Price.

Howard wrote with enormous energy and force. His
stories were told with gusto and verve, drenched in vivid
primary colors, filled with the thrill of excitement and
adventure. Through his haunted, jungle-clad ruins and
barbaric prehistoric cities move towering and indomitable

warriors, cunning and malefic sorcerers and women of voluptuous and breath-taking beauty.

His first creations were Bran Mak Morn, who led the Caledonian Picts up against the iron legions of Imperial Rome, and Solomon Kane, a dour Puritan adventurer who cut a bloody path through darkest Africa, battling savage warriors and cruel witch-doctors. But Howard was not quite easy working in known historical and geographical limitations: he yearned to bust loose and build worlds to his own design. This he did quite early, with his tales of the Atlantean savage Kull, who rose to the throne of prehistoric Valusia, and with his much more famous tales of Conan the giant Cimmerian hero of the lost, forgotten Hyborean Age.

In such stories, he devised an imaginary world that had existed many thousands of years before the rise of Egypt and Chaldea. It was his rather clever idea that half-remembered fragments of this primal world lingered into historical time as the basis of the mythologies of early civilization (such as his "River Styx" which gave its name to the dark kingdom of sorcerers he calls "Stygia" —prehistoric Egypt and the river Nile, that is).

Howard rapidly became a very successful writer. By his late twenties he was not only making a decent living out of magazine fiction, but he was actually earning more money than any of the 1,500 other people in Cross Plains —including the town banker! And he outgrew his early fragility as well. In his prime, Howard was not unlike one of his own stalwart characters. He stood six feet tall and weighed over two hundred pounds, and most of that was solid muscle. His unhealthy attachment to his mother ended a very promising career: he suicided upon learning of her death.

Howard's conception of a mythic age and a prehistoric world is one of the legitimate variations on the imaginary world theme, and I wanted one of his stories for this representative collection. But the Conan and Kull stories are well-known and available, so I selected a less familiar tale from the February, 1934, issue of *Weird Tales*. In it we see Howard's conception of the original of the legend of the Dragon Killer. He himself points out that the tale

of Niord and his epic battle with the giant Worm lived
on in man's memory to become the ultimate source of the
famous exploits of Perseus, Beowulf, Siegfried and St.
George. This story also exemplifies Howard's great talent
for writing, his vigor and drive and raw elemental
power . . . .

I WILL tell you of Niord and the Worm. You have
heard the tale before in many guises wherein the hero
was named Tyr, or Perseus, or Beowulf, or Saint George.
But it was Niord who met the loathly demoniac thing
that crawled hideously up from hell, and from which
meeting sprang the cycle of hero-tales that revolves
down the ages until the very substance of the truth is
lost and passes into the limbo of all forgotten legends. I
know whereof I speak, for I was Niord.

As I lie here awaiting death, which creeps slowly
upon me like a blind slug, my dreams are filled with
glittering visions and the pageantry of glory. It is not of
the drab, disease-wracked life of James Allison I dream,
but all the gleaming figures of the mighty pageantry that
have passed before, and shall come after; for I have
faintly glimpsed, not merely the shapes that trail out behind, but shapes that shall come after, as a man in a
long parade glimpses, far ahead, the line of figures that
precede him winding over a distant hill, etched
shadow-like against the sky. I am one and all the pageantry of shapes and guises and masks which have
been, are, and shall be the visible manifestations of that
illusive, intangible, but vitally existent spirit now prom-
enading under the brief and temporary name of James
Allison.

Each man on earth, each woman, is part and all of a
similar caravan of shapes and beings. But they cannot
remember—their minds cannot bridge the brief, awful
gulfs of blackness which lie between those unstable

shapes, and which the spirit, soul, or ego, in spanning, shakes off its fleshly masks. I remember. Why I can remember is the strangest tale of all; but as I lie here with death's black wings slowly unfolding over me, all the dim folds of my previous lives are shaken out before my eyes, and I see myself in many forms and guises—braggart, swaggering, fearful, loving, foolish, all that men have been or will be.

I have been Man in many lands and many conditions; yet—and here is another strange thing—my line of reincarnation runs straight down one unerring channel. I have never been any but a man of that restless race men once called Nordheimr and later Aryans, and today name by many names and designations. Their history is my history, from the first mewling wail of a hairless white ape cub in the wastes of the arctic, to the death-cry of the last degenerate product of ultimate civilization, in some dim and unguessed future age.

My name has been Hialmar, Tyr, Bragi, Bran, Horsa, Eric, and John. I strode red-handed through the deserted streets of Rome behind the yellow-maned Brennus; I wandered through the violated plantations with Alaric and his Goths when the flame of burning villas lit the land like day and an empire was gasping its last under our sandaled feet; I waded sword in hand through the foaming surf from Hengist's galley to lay the foundations of England in blood and pillage; when Leif the Lucky sighted the broad white beaches of an unguessed world, I stood beside him in the bows of the dragon-ship, my golden beard blowing in the wind; and when Godfrey of Bouillon led his Crusaders over the walls of Jerusalem, I was among them in steel cap and brigandine.

But it is of none of these things I would speak. I would take you back with me into an age beside which that of Brennus and Rome is as yesterday. I would take you back through, not merely centuries and millenniums, but epochs and dim ages unguessed by the wildest philosopher. Oh far, far and far will you fare into the nighted Past before you win beyond the boundaries of my race, blue-eyed, yellow-haired, slayers, lovers, mighty in rapine and wayfaring.

It is the adventure of Niord Worm's-bane of which I would speak—the root-stem of a whole cycle of hero-tales which has not yet reached its end, the grisly under-lying reality that lurks behind time-distorted myths of dragons, fiends, and monsters.

Yet it is not alone with the mouth of Niord that I will speak. I am James Allison no less than I was Niord, and as I unfold the tale, I will interpret some of his thoughts and dreams and deeds from the mouth of the modern I, so that the saga of Niord shall not be a meaningless chaos to you. His blood is your blood, who are sons of Aryan; but wide misty gulfs of eons lie horrifically be-tween, and the deeds and dreams of Niord seem as alien to your deeds and dreams as the primordial and lion-haunted forest seems alien to the white-walled city street.

It was a strange world in which Hiord lived and loved and fought, so long ago that even my eon-spanning mem-ory can not recognize landmarks. Since then the surface of the earth has changed, not once but a score of times; continents have risen and sunk, seas have changed their beds and rivers their courses, glaciers have waxed and waned, and the very stars and constellations have al-tered and shifted.

It was so long ago that the cradle-land of my race was still in Nordheim. But the epic drifts of my people had already begun, and blue-eyed, yellow-maned tribes flowed eastward and southward and westward, on cen-tury-long treks that carried them about the world and left their bones and their traces in strange lands and wild waste places. On one of these drifts I grew from in-fancy to manhood. My knowledge of that northern homeland was dim memories, like half-remembered dreams, of blinding white snow plains and ice-fields, of great fires roaring n the circle of hide tents, of yellow manes flying in great winds, and a sun setting in a lurid wallow of crimson clouds, blazing on trampled snow where still dark forms lay in pools that were redder than the sunset.

That last memory stands out clearer than the others. It was the field of Jotunheim, I was told in later years, whereon had just been fought that terrible battle which was the Armageddon of the Aesir-folk, the subject of a cycle of hero-songs for long ages, and which still lives today in dim dreams of Ragnarok and Götterdämmerung. I looked on that battle as a mewling infant; so I must have lived about—but I will not name the age, for I would be called a madman, and historians and geologists alike would rise to dispute me.

But my memories of Nordheim were few and dim, paled by memories of that long long trek upon which I had spent my life. We had not kept to a straight course, but our trend had been forever southward. Sometimes we had bided for a while in fertile upland valleys or rich river-traversed plains, but always we took up the trail again, and not always because of drouth or famine. Often we left countries teeming with game and wild grain to push into wastelands. On our trail we moved endlessly, driven only by our restless whim, yet blindly following a cosmic law, the workings of which we never guessed, any more than the wild geese guess in their flights around the world. So at last we came into the Country of the Worm.

I will take up the tale at the time when we came into the jungle-clad hills reeking with rot and teeming with spawning life, where the tom-toms of a savage people pulsed incessantly through the hot breathless night. These people came forth to dispute our way—short, strongly built men, black-haired, painted, ferocious, but indisputably white men. We knew their breed of old. They were Picts, and of all alien races, the fiercest. We had met their kind before in thick forests, and in upland valleys beside mountain lakes. But many moons had passed since those meetings.

I believe this particular tribe represented the easternmost drift of the race. They were the most primitive and ferocious of any I ever met. Already they were exhibiting hints of characteristics I have noted among black savages in jungle countries, though they had dwelt in these environs only a few generations. The abysmal jungle was engulfing them, was obliterating their pristine characteristics and shaping them in its own horrific mold. They were drifting into head-hunting and cannibalism was but a step which I believe they must have taken before they became extinct. These things are natural adjuncts to the jungle; the Picts did not learn them from the black people, for then there were no blacks among those hills. In later years they came up from the south, and the Picts first enslaved and then were absorbed by them. But with that my saga of Niord is not concerned.

We came into that brutish hill country, with its squalling abysms of savagery and black primitiveness. We were a whole tribe marching on foot, old men, wolfish with their long beards and gaunt limbs, giant warriors in their prime, naked children running along the line of march, women with tousled yellow locks carrying babies which never cried—unless it were to scream from pure rage. I do not remember our numbers, except that there were some five hundred fightingmen—and by fightingmen I mean all males, from the child just strong enough to lift a bow, to the oldest of the old men. In that madly ferocious age all were fighters. Our women fought, when brought to bay, like tigresses, and I have seen a babe, not yet old enough to stammer articulate words, twist its head and sink its teeth in the foot that stamped out its life.

Oh, we were fighters! Let me speak of Niord. I am proud of him, the more when I consider the paltry crippled body of James Allison, the unstable mask I now wear. Niord was tall, with great shoulders, lean hips, and mighty limbs. His muscles were long and swelling, denoting endurance and speed as well as strength. He could run all day without tiring, and he possessed a coordination that made his movements a blur of blinding speed. If I told you of his full strength, you would brand me a liar. But there is no man on earth today strong enough to bend the bow Niord handled with ease. The longest arrow-flight on record is that of a Turkish archer who sent a shaft 482 yards. There was not a stripling in my tribe who could not have bettered that flight.

As we entered the jungle country we heard the tom-toms booming across the mysterious valley that slumbered between the brutish hills, and in a broad, open plateau we met our enemies. I do not believe these Picts knew us, even by legends, or they had never rushed so openly to the onset, though they out-numbered us. But there was no attempt at ambush. They swarmed out of the trees, dancing and singing their war-songs, yelling their barbarous threats. Our heads should hang in their idol-hut and our yellow-haired women should bear their sons. Ho! ho! ho! By Ymir, it was Niord who laughed then, not James Allison. Just so we of the Aesir laughed to hear their threats—deep thunderous laughter from broad and mighty chests. Our trail was laid in blood and embers through many lands. We were the slayers and ravishers, striding sword in hand across the world, and that these folk threatened us woke our rugged humor.

We went to meet them, naked but for our wolfhides, swinging our bronze swords, and our singing was like rolling thunder in the hills. They sent their arrows among us, as and we gave back their fire. They could not match us in archery. Our arrows hissed in blinding clouds among them, dropping them like autumn leaves, until they howled and frothed like mad dogs and charged to hand-grips. And we, mad with the fighting joy, dropped our bows and ran to meet them, as a lover runs to his love.

By Ymir, it was a battle to madden and make drunken with the slaughter and the fury. The Picts were as ferocious as we, but ours was the superior physique, the keener wit, the more highly-developed fighting-brain. We won because we were a superior race, but it was no easy victory. Corpses littered the blood-soaked earth; but at last they broke, and we cut them down as they ran, to the very edge of the trees. I tell of that fight in a few bald words. I can not paint the madness, the reek of sweat and blood, the panting, muscle-straining effort, the splintering of bones under mighty blows, the rending and hewing of quivering sentient flesh; above all the merciless abysmal savagery of the whole affair, in which there was neither rule nor order, each man fighting as he would or could. If I might do so, you could recoil in horror; even the modern I, cognizant of my close kinship with those times, stands aghast as I review that butchery. Mercy was yet unborn, save as some individual's whim, and rules of warfare were as yet undreamed of. It was an age in which each tribe and each human fought tooth and fang from birth to death, and neither gave or expected mercy.

So we cut down the fleeing Picts, and our women came out on the field to brain the wounded enemies with stones, or cut their throats with copper knives. We did not torture. We were no more cruel than life demanded. The rule of life was ruthlessness, but there is more wanton cruelty today that ever we dreamed of. It was not wanton bloodthirstiness that made us butcher wounded and captive foes. It was because we knew our chances of survival increased with each enemy slain.

Yet there was occasionally a touch of individual mercy, and so it was in this fight. I had been occupied with a duel with an especially valiant enemy. His tousled thatch of black hair scarcely came above my chin, but he was a solid knot of steel-spring muscles, than which lightning scarcely moved faster. He had an iron sword and a hide-covered buckler. I had a knotty-headed bludgeon. That fight was one that glutted even my battle-lusting soul. It was bleeding from a score of flesh wounds before one of my terrible lashing strokes glanced from his unprotected head. Ymir! Even now I stop to laugh and marvel at the hardness of that Pict's skull. Men of that age were assuredly built on a rugged plan! That blow should have spattered his brains like water. It did lay his scalp open horribly, dashing him senseless to earth, where I let him lie, supposing him to be dead, as I joined in the slaughter of the fleeing warriors.

When I returned reeking with sweat and blood, my club horribly clotted with blood and brains, I noticed that my antagonist was regaining consciousness, and that a naked tousle-headed girl was preparing to give him the finishing touch with a stone she could scarcely lift. A vagrant whim caused me to check the blow. I had enjoyed the fight, and I admired the adamantine quality of his skull.

We made camp a short distance away, burned our dead on a great pyre, and after looting the corpses of the enemy, we dragged them across the plateau and cast them down in a valley to make a feast for the hyenas, jackals, and vultures which were already gathering. We kept close watch that night, but we were not attacked, though far away through the jungle we could make out the red gleam of fires, and could faintly hear, when the wind veered, the throb of tom-toms and demoniac screams and yells—keenings for the slain or mere animal squallings of fury.

Nor did they attack us in the days that followed. We bandaged our captive's wounds and quickly learned his primitive tongue, which, however, was so different from ours that I can not conceive of the two languages having ever had a common source.

His name was Grom, and he was a great hunter and fighter, he boasted. He talked freely and held no grudge, grinning broadly and showing tusk-like teeth, his beady eyes glittering from under the tangled black mane that fell over his low forehead. His limbs were almost ape-like in their thickness.

He was vastly interested in his captors, though he could never understand why he had been spared; to the end it remained an inexplicable mystery to him. The Picts obeyed the law of survival even more rigidly than did the Aesir. They were the more practical, as shown by their more settled habits. They never roamed as far or as blindly as we. Yet in every line we were the superior race.

Grom, impressed by our intelligence and fighting qualities, volunteered to go into the hills and make peace for us with his people. It was immaterial to us, but we let him go. Slavery had not yet been dreamed of.

So Grom went back to his people, and we forgot about him, except that I went a trifle more cautiously about my hunting, expecting him to be lying in wait to put an arrow through my back. Then one day we heard a rattle of tom-toms, and Grom appeared at the edge of the jungle, his face split in his gorilla-grin, with the painted, skin-clad, feather-bedecked chiefs of the clans. Our ferocity awed them, and our sparing of Grom further impressed them. They could not understand leniency; evidently we valued them too cheaply to bother about killing one when he was in our power.

So peace was made with much pow-wow, and sworn to with many strange oaths and rituals—we swore only by Ymir, and an Aesir never broke that vow. But they swore by the elements, by the idol which sat in the fetish-hut where fires burned for ever and a withered crone slapped a leather-covered drum all night long, and by another being too terrible to be named.

Then we all sat around the fires and gnawed meat-bones, and drank a fiery concoction they brewed from wild grain, and the wonder is that the feast did not end in a general massacre; for that liquor had devils in it, and made maggots writhe in our brains. But no harm came of our vast drunkenness, and thereafter we dwelt at peace with our barbarous neighbors. They taught us many things, and learned many more from us. But they taught us iron-working, into which they had been forced by lack of copper in those hills, and we quickly excelled them.

We went freely among their villages—mud-walled clusters of huts in hilltop clearings, overshadowed by giant trees—and we allowed them to come at will among our camps—straggling lines of hide tents on the plateau where the battle had been fought. Our young men cared not for their squat beady-eyed women, and our rangy clean-limbed girls with their tousled yellow heads were not drawn to the hairy-breasted savages. Familiarity over a period of years would have reduced the repulsion on either side, until the two races would have flowed together to form one hybrid people, but long before that time the Aesir rose and departed, vanishing into the mysterious hazes of the haunted south. But before that exodus there came to pass the horror of the Worm.

I hunted with Grom and he led me into brooding, uninhabited valleys and up into silence-haunted hills where no men had set foot before us. But there was one valley, off in the mazes of the southwest, into which he would not go. Stumps of shattered columns, relics of a forgotten civilization, stood among the trees on the valley floor. Grom showed them to me, as we stood on the cliffs that flanked the mysterious vale, but he would not go down into it, and he dissuaded me when I would have gone alone. He would not speak plainly of the danger that lurked there, but it was greater than that of serpent or tiger, or the trumpeting elephants which occasionally wandered up in devastating droves from the south.

Of all beasts, Grom told me in the gutturals of his tongue, the Picts feared only Satha, the great snake, and they shunned the jungle where he lived. But there was another thing they feared, and it was connected in some manner with the Valley of Broken Stones, as the Picts called the crumbling pillars. Long ago, when his ancestors had first come into the country, they had dared that grim vale, and a whole clan of them had perished, suddenly, horribly, and unexplainably. At least Grom did not not explain. The horror had come up out of the earth, somehow, and it was not good to talk of it, since it was believed that It might be summoned by speaking of It—whatever It was.

But Grom was ready to hunt with me anywhere else; for he was the greatest hunter among the Picts, and many and fearful were our adventures. Once I killed, with the iron sword I had forged with my own hands, that most terrible of all beasts—old sabre-tooth, which men today call a tiger because he was more like a tiger than anything else. In reality he was almost as much like a bear in build, save for his unmistakably feline head. Sabre-tooth was massive-limbed, with a long-hung, great, heavy body, and he vanished from the earth because he was too terrible a fighter, even for that grim age. As his muscles and ferocity grew, his brain dwindled until at last even the instinct of self-preservation vanished. Nature, who maintains her balance in such things, destroyed him because, had his super-fighting powers been allied with an intelligent brain, he would have destroyed all other forms of life on earth. He was a freak on the road of evolution—organic development gone mad and run to fangs and talons, to slaughter and destruction.

I killed sabre-tooth in a battle that would make a saga in itself, and for months afterward I lay semi-delirious with ghastly wounds that made the toughest warriors shake their heads. The Picts said that never before had a man killed a sabre-tooth single-handed. Yet I recovered, to the wonder of all.

While I lay at the doors of death there was a secession from the tribe. It was a peaceful secession, such as continually occurred and contributed greatly to the peopling of the world by yellow-haired tribes. Forty-five of the young men took themselves mates simultaneously and wandered off to found a clan of their own. There was no revolt; it was a racial custom which bore fruit in all the later ages, when tribes sprung from the same roots met, after centuries of separation, and cut one another's throats with joyous abandon. The tendency of the Aryan and the pre-Aryan was always toward disunity, clans splitting off the main stem, and scattering.

So these young men, led by one Bragi, my brother-in-arms, took their girls and venturing to the southwest, took up their abode in the Valley of Broken Stones. The Picts expostulated, hinting vaguely of a monstrous doom that haunted the vale, but the Aesir laughed. We had left our own demons and weirds in the icy wastes of the far blue north, and the devils of other races did not much impress us.

When my full strength was returned, and the grisly wounds were only scars, I girt on my weapons and strode over the plateau to visit Bragi's clan. Grom did not accompany me. He had not been in the Aesir camp for several days. But I knew the way. I remembered well the valley, from the cliffs of which I had looked down and seen the lake at the upper end, the trees thickening into forest at the lower extremity. The sides of the valley were high sheer cliffs, and a steep broad ridge at either end cut it off from the surrounding country. It was toward the lower or southwestern end that the valley-floor was dotted thickly with ruined columns, some towering high among the trees, some fallen into heaps of lichen-clad stones. What race reared them none knew. But Grom had hinted fearsomely of a hairy, apish monstrosity dancing loathsomely under the moon to a demoniac piping that induced horror and madness.

I crossed the plateau whereon our camp was pitched, descended the slope, traversed a shallow vegetation-choked valley, climbed another slope, and plunged into the hills. A half-day's leisurely travel brought me to the ridge on the other side of which lay the valley of the pillars. For many miles I had seen no sign of human life. The settlements of the Picts all lay many miles to the east. I topped the ridge and looked down into the dreaming valley with its still blue lake, its brooding cliffs, and its broken columns jutting among the trees. I looked for smoke. I saw none, but I saw vultures wheeling in the sky over a cluster of tents on the lake shore.

I came down the ridge warily, and approached the silent camp. In it I halted, frozen with horror. I was not easily moved. I had seen death in many forms, and had fled from or taken part in red massacres that spilled blood like water and heaped the earth with corpses. But here I was confronted with an organic devastation that staggered and appalled me. Of Bragi's embryonic clan, not one remained alive, and not one corpse was whole. Some of the hide-tents still stood erect. Others were mashed down and flattened out, as if crushed by some monstrous weight, so that at first I wondered if a drove of elephants had stampeded across the camp. But no elephants ever wrought such destruction as I saw strewn on the bloody ground. The camp was a shambles, littered with bits of flesh and fragments of bodies— hands, feet, heads, pieces of human debris. Weapons lay about, some of them stained with a greenish slime like that which spurts from a crushed caterpillar.

No human foe could have committed this ghastly atrocity. I looked at the lake, wondering if nameless amphibian monsters had crawled from the calm waters whose deep blue told of unfathomed depths. Then I saw a print left by the destroyer. It was a track such as a titanic worm might leave, yards broad, winding back down the valley. The grass lay flat where it ran, and bushes and small trees had been crushed down into the earth, all horribly smeared with blood and greenish slime.

With berserk fury in my soul I drew my sword and started to follow it, when a call attracted me. I wheeled, to see a stocky form approaching me from the ridge. It was Grom the Pict, and when I think of the courage it must have taken for him to overcome all the instincts planted in him by traditional teachings and personal experience, I realize the full depths of his friendship for me.

Squatting tn the lake short, spear in his hands, his black eyes ever roving fearfully down the brooding tree-waving reaches of the valley, Grom told me of the horror that had come upon Bragi's clan under the moon. But first he told me of it, as his sires had told the tale to him.

Long ago the Picts had drifted down from the northwest on a long, long trek, finally reaching these jungle-covered hills, where, because they were weary, and because the game and fruit were plentiful and there were no hostile tribes, they halted and built their mud-walled villages.

Some of them, a whole clan of that numerous tribe, took up their abode in the Valley of the Broken Stones. They found the columns and a great ruined temple back in the trees, and in that temple there was no shrine or altar, but the mouth of a shaft that vanished deep into the black earth, and in which there were no steps such as a human would make and use. They built their village in the valley, and in the night, under the moon, horror came upon them and left only broken walls and bits of slime-smeared flesh.

In those days the Picts feared nothing. The warriors of the other clans gathered and sang their war-songs and danced their war dances, and followed a broad track of blood and slime to the shaft-mouth in the temple. They howled defiance and hurled down boulders which were never heard to strike bottom. Then began a thin demoniac piping, and up from the well pranced a hideous anthropomorphic figure dancing to the weird strains of a pipe it held in its monstrous paws. The horror of its aspect froze the fierce Picts with amazement, and close behind it a vast white bulk heaved up from the subterranean darkness. Out of the shaft came a slavering mad nightmare which arrows pierced but could not check, which swords carved but could not slay. It fell slobbering upon the warriors, crushing them to crimson pulp, tearing them to bits as an octopus might tear small fishes, sucking their blood from their mangled limbs and devouring them even as they screamed and struggled. The survivors fled, pursued to the very ridge, up which, apparently, the monster could not propel its quaking mountainous bulk.

After that they did not dare the silent valley. But the dead came to their shamans and old men in dreams and told them strange and terrible secrets. They spoke of an ancient, ancient race of semi-human beings which once inhabited that valley and reared those columns for their own weird inexplicable purpose. The white monster in the pits was their god, summoned up from the nighted abysses of mid-earth uncounted fathoms below the black mold, by sorcery unknown to the sons of men. The hairy

anthropomorphic being was its servant, created to serve
the god, a formless elemental spirit drawn up from below
and cased in flesh, organic but beyond the understanding of humanity. The Old Ones had long vanished into
the limbo from whence they crawled in the black dawn
of the universe, but their bestial god and his inhuman
slave lived on. Yet both were organic after a fashion,
and could be wounded, though no human weapon had
been found potent enough to slay them.

Bragi and his clan had dwelt for weeks in the valley
before the horror struck. Only the night before, Grom,
hunting above the cliffs, and by that token daring
greatly, had been paralyzed by a high-pitched demon
piping, and then by a mad clamor of human screaming.
Stretched face down in the dirt, hiding his head in a
tangle of grass, he had not dared to move, even when
the shrieks died away in the slobbering, repulsive
sounds of a hideous feast. When dawn broke he had
crept shuddering to the cliffs to look down into the valley, and the sight of the devastation, even when seen
from afar, had driven him in yammering flight far into
the hills. But it had occurred to him, finally, that he
should warn the rest of the tribe, and returning, on his
way to the camp on the plateau, he had seen me entering the valley.

So spoke Grom, while I sat and brooded darkly, my
chin on my mighty fist. I can not frame in modern words
the clan-feeling that in those days was a living vital part
of every man and woman. In a world where talon and
fang were lifted on every hand, and the hands of all
men raised against an individual, except those of his
own clan, tribal instinct was more than the phrase it is
today. It was as much a part of a man as was his heart
or his right hand. This was necessary, for only thus
banded together in unbreakable groups could mankind
have survived in the terrible environments of the primitive world. So now the personal grief I felt for Bragi and
the clean-limbed young men and laughing white-skinned
girls was drowned in a deeper sea of grief and fury that
was cosmic in its depth and intensity. I sat grimly, while

the Pict squatted anxiously beside me, his gaze roving from me to the menacing deeps of the valley where the accursed columns loomed like broken teeth of cackling hags among the waving leafy reaches.

I, Niord, was not one to use my brain over-much. I lived in a physical world, and there were the old men of the tribe to do my thinking. But I was one of a race destined to become dominant mentally as well as physically, and I was no mere muscular animal. So as I sat there there came dimly and then clearly a thought to me that brought a short fierce laugh from my lips.

Rising, I bade Grom aid me, and we built a pyre on the lake shore of dried wood, the ridge-poles of the tents, and the broken shafts of spears. Then we collected the grisly fragments that had been parts of Bragi's band, and we laid them on the pile, and struck flint and steel to it.

The thick sad smoke crawled serpent-like into the sky, and turning to Grom, I made him guide me to the jungle wherein lurked that scaly horror, Satha, the great serpent. Grom gaped at me; not the greatest hunter among the Picts sought out the mighty crawling one. But my will was like a wind that swept him along my course, and at last he led the way. We left the valley by the upper end, crossing the ridge, skirting the tall cliffs, and plunged into the vastnesses of the south, which was peopled only by the grim denizens of the jungle. Deep into the jungle we went, until we came to a low-lying expanse, dark and dark beneath the great creeper-festooned trees, where our feet sank deep into the spongy silt, carpeted by rotting vegetation, and slimy moisture oozed up beneath their pressure. This, Grom told me, was the realm haunted by Satha, the great serpent.

Let me speak of Satha. There is nothing like him on earth today, nor has there been for countless ages. Like the meat-eating dinosaur, like old sabre-tooth, he was too terrible to exist. Even then he was a survival of a grimmer age when life and its forms were cruder and more hideous. There were not many of his kind then, though they may have existed in great numbers in the reeking ooze of the vast jungle-tangled swamps still far-ther south. He was larger than any python of modern ages, and his fangs dripped with poison a thousand times more deadly than that of a king cobra.

He was never worshipped by the pure-blood Picts, though the blacks that came later deified him, and that adoration persisted in the hybrid race that sprang from the Negroes and their white conquerors. But to other peoples he was the nadir of evil horror, and tales of him became twisted into demonology; so in later ages Satha became the veritable devil of the white races, and the Stygians first worshipped, and then, when they became Egyptians, abhorred him under the name of Set, the Old Serpent, while to the Semites he became Leviathan and Satan. He was terrible enough to be a god, for he was a crawling death. I had seen a bull elephant fall dead in his tracks from Satha's bite. I had seen him, had glimpsed him writhing his horrific way through the dense jungle, had seen him take his prey, but had never hunted him. He was too grim, even for the slayer of old sabre-tooth.

But now I hunted him, plunging farther and farther into the hot, breathless reek of his jungle, even when friendship for me could not drive Grom farther. He urged me to paint my body and sing my death-song be-fore I advanced farther, but I pushed on unheeding.

In a natural runway that wound between the shoul-dering trees, I set a trap. I found a large tree, soft and spongy of fibre, but thick-boled and heavy, and I hacked through its base close to the ground with my great sword, directing its fall so that when it toppled, its top crashed into the branches of a smaller tree, leaving it leaning across the runway, one end resting on the earth, the other caught in the small tree. Then I cut away the branches on the under side, and cutting a slim tough sap-ling I trimmed it and stuck it upright like a prop-pole under the leaning tree. Then, cutting away the tree which supported it, I left the great trunk posied preca-riously on the prop-pole, to which I fastened a long vine as thick as my wrist.

Then I went alone through the primordial twilight jungle until an over-powering fetid odor assailed my nostrils, and from the rank vegetation in front of me, Satha reared up his hideous head, swaying letally from side to side, while his forked tongue jetted in and out, and his great yellow terrible eyes burned icily on me with all the evil wisdom of the black elder world that was when man was not. I backed away, feeling no fear, only an icy sensation along my spine, and Satha came sinuously after me, his shining eighty-foot barrel rippling over the rotting vegetation in mesmeric silence. His wedge-shaped head was bigger than the head of the hugest stallion, his trunk was thicker than a man's body and his scales shimmered with a thousand changing scintillations. I was to Satha as a mouse is to a king cobra, but I was fanged as no mouse ever was. Quick as I was, I knew I could not avoid the lightning stroke of that great triangular head; so I dared not let him come too close. Subtly I fled down the runway, and behind me the rush of the great supple body was like the sweep of wind through the grass.

He was not far behind me when I raced beneath the deadfall, and as the great shining length glided under the trap, I gripped the vine with both hands and jerked desperately. With a crash the great trunk fell across Satha's scaly back, some six feet back of his wedge-shaped head.

I had hoped to break his spine but I do not think I did, for the great body coiled and knotted, the mighty tail lashed and thrashed, mowing down the bushes as if with a giant flail. At the instant of the fall, the huge head had whipped about and struck the tree with a terrific impact, the mighty fangs shearing through bark and wood like scimitars. Now, as if aware he fought an inanimate foe, Satha turned on me, standing out of his reach. The scaly neck writhed and arched, the mighty jaws gaped, disclosing fangs a foot in length, from which dripped venom that might have burned through solid stone.

I believe, what of his stupendous strength, that Satha

would have writhed from under the trunk, but for a broken branch that had been driven deep into his side, holding him like a barb. The sound of his hissing filled the jungle and his eyes glared at me with such concentrated evil that I shook despite myself. Oh, he knew it was I who had trapped him! Now I came as close as I dared, and with a sudden powerful cast of my spear, transfixed his neck just below the gaping jaws, nailing him to the tree-trunk. Then I dared greatly, for he was far from dead, and I knew he would in an instant tear the spear from the wood and be free to strike. But in that instant I ran in, and swinging my sword with all my great power, I hewed off his terrible head.

The heavings and contortions of Satha's prisoned form in life were naught to the convulsions of his headless length in death. I retreated, dragging the gigantic head after me with a crooked pole, and a safe distance from the lashing, flying tail, I set to work. I worked with naked death then, and no man ever toiled more gingerly than I did. For I cut out the poison sacs at the base of the great fangs, and in that terrible venom I soaked the heads of eleven arrows, being careful that only the bronze points were in the liquid, which else had corroded away the wood of the tough shafts. While I was doing this, Grom, driven by his comradeship and curiosity, came stealing nervously through the jungle, and his mouth gaped as he looked on the head of Satha.

For hours I steeped the arrowheads in the poison, until they were caked with a horrible green scum, and showed tiny flecks of corrosion where the venom had eaten into the solid bronze. I wrapped them carefully in broad, thick, rubber-like leaves, and then, though night had fallen and the hunting beasts were roaring on every hand, I went back through the jungled hills, Grom with me, until at dawn we came again to the high cliffs that loomed above the Valley of Broken Stones.

At the mouth of the valley I broke my spear, and I took all the unpoisoned shafts from my quiver, and snapped them. I painted my face and limbs as the Aesir painted themselves only when they went forth to certain doom, and I sang my death-song to the sun as it rose over the cliffs, my yellow mane blowing in the morning wind.

Then I went down into the valley, bow in hand.

Grom could not drive himself to follow me. He lay on his belly in the dust and howled like a dying dog.

I passed the lake and the silent camp where the pyre-ashes still smouldered, and came under the thickening trees beyond. About me the columns loomed, mere shapeless heaps from the ravages of staggering eons. The trees grew more dense, and under their vast leafy branches the very light was dusky and evil. As in twilight shadow I saw the ruined temple, cyclopean walls staggering up from masses of decaying masonry and fallen blocks of stone. About six hundred yards in front of it a great column reared up in an open glade, eighty or ninety feet in height. It was so worn and pitted by weather and time that any child of my tribe could have climbed it, and I marked it and changed my plan.

I came to the ruins and saw huge crumbling walls upholding a domed roof from which many stones had fallen, so that it seemed like the lichen-grown ribs of some mythical monster's skeleton arching above me. Titanic columns flanked an open doorway through which ten elephants could have stalked abreast. Once there might have been inscriptions and hieroglyphics on the pillars and walls, but they were long worn away. Around the great room, on the inner side, ran columns in better state of preservation. On each of these columns was a flat pedestal, and some dim instinctive memory vaguely resurrected a shadowy scene wherein black drums roared madly and on these pedestals monstrous beings squatted loathsomely in inexplicable rituals rooted in the black dawn of the universe.

There was no altar—only the mouth of a great well-like shaft in the stone floor, with strange obscene carvings all about the rim. I tore great pieces of stone from the rotting floor and cast them down the shaft which slanted down into utter darkness. I heard them bound along the side, but I did not hear them strike bottom. I cast down stone after stone, each with a searing curse, and at last I heard a sound that was not the dwindling rumble of the falling stones. Up from the well floated a weird demon-piping that was a symphony of madness. Far down in the darkness I glimpsed the faint fearful glimmering of a vast white bulk.

I retreated slowly as the piping grew louder, falling back through the broad doorway. I heard a scratching, scrambling noise, and up from the shaft and out of the doorway between the colossal columns came a prancing incredible figure. It went erect like a man, but it was covered with fur, that was shaggiest where its face should have been. If it had ears, nose, and a mouth I did not discover them. Only a pair of staring red eyes leered from the furry mask. Its misshapen hands held a strange set of pipes, on which it blew weirdly as it pranced toward me with many a grotesque caper and leap.

Behind it I heard a repulsive obscene noise as of a quaking unstable mass heaving up out of a well. Then I nocked an arrow, drew the cord and sent the shaft singing through the furry breast of the dancing monstrosity. It went down as though struck by a thunderbolt, but to my horror the piping continued, though the pipes had fallen from the malformed hands. Then I turned and ran fleetly to the column, up which I swarmed before I looked back. When I reached the pinnacle I looked, and because of the shock and surprise of what I saw, I almost fell from my dizzy perch.

Out of the temple the monstrous dweller in the darkness had come, and I, who had expected a horror yet cast in some terrestrial mold, looked on the spawn of nightmare. From what subterranean hell it crawled in the long ago I know not, nor what black age it represented. But it was not a beast, as humanity knows beasts. I call it a worm for lack of a better term. There is no earthly language which has a name for it. I can only say it looked somewhat more like a worm than it did an octopus, a serpent or a dinosaur.

It was white and pulpy, and drew its quaking bulk along the ground, worm-fashion. But it had wide flat tentacles, and fleshy feelers, and other adjuncts the use of which I am unable to explain. And it had a long proboscis which it curled and uncurled like an elephant's trunk. Its forty eyes, set in a horrific circle, were composed of thousands of facets of as many scintillant colors which changed and altered in never-ending transmutation. But through all interplay of hue and glint, they retained their evil intelligence—intelligence there was behind those flickering facets, not human nor yet bestial, but a night-born demoniac intelligence such as men in dreams vaguely sense throbbing titanically in the black gulfs outside our material universe. In size the monster was mountainous; its bulk would have dwarfed a mastodon.

But even as I shook with the cosmic horror of the thing, I drew a feathered shaft to my ear and arched it singing on its way. Grass and bushes were crushed flat as the monster came toward me like a moving mountain and shaft after shaft I sent with terrific force and deadly precision. I could not miss so huge a target. The arrows sank to the feathers or clear out of sight in the unstable bulk, each bearing enough poison to have stricken dead a bull elephant. Yet on it came, swiftly, appallingly, apparently heedless of both the shafts and the venom in which they were steeped. And all the time the hideous music played a maddening accompaniment, whining thinly from the pipes that lay untouched on the ground.

My confidence faded; even the poison of Satha was futile against this uncanny being. I drove my last shaft almost straight downward into the quaking white mountain, so close was the monster under my perch. Then suddenly its color altered. A wave of ghastly blue surged over it, and the vast bulk heaved in earthquake-like convulsions. With a terrible plunge it struck the lower part of the column which crashed to falling shards of stone. But even with the impact, I leaped far out and fell through the empty air full upon the monster's back.

The spongy skin yielded and gave beneath my feet, and I drove my sword hilt-deep, dragging it through the pulpy flesh, ripping a horrible yard-long wound, from which oozed a green slime. Then a flip of a cable-like tentacle flicked me from the titan's back and spun me three hundred feet through the air to crash among a cluster of giant trees.

The impact must have splintered half the bones in my frame, for when I sought to grasp my sword again and crawl anew to the combat, I could not move hand or foot, could only writhe helplessly with my broken back. But I could see the monster and I knew that I had won, even in defeat. The mountainous bulk was heaving and billowing, the tentacles were lashing madly, and the antennae writhing and knotting, and the nauseous whiteness had changed to a pale and grisly green. It turned ponderously and lurched back toward the temple, rolling like a crippled ship in a heavy swell. Trees crashed and splintered as it lumbered against them.

I wept with pure fury because I could not catch up my sword and rush in to die glutting my berserk madness in mighty strokes. But the worm-god was death-stricken and needed not my futile sword. The demon pipes on the ground kept up their infernal tune, and it was like the fiend's death-dirge. Then as the monster veered and floundered, I saw it catch up the corpse of its hairy slave. For an instant the apish form dangled in midair, gripped round by the trunk-like proboscis, then was dashed against the temple wall with a force that reduced the hairy body to a mere shapeless pulp. At that the pipes screamed out horribly, and fell silent forever.

The titan staggered on the brink of the shaft; then another change came over it—a frightful transfiguration the nature of which I can not yet describe. Even now when I try to think of it clearly, I am only chaotically conscious of a blasphemous, unnatural transmutation of form and substance, shocking and indescribable. Then the strangely altered bulk tumbled into the shaft to roll down into the ultimate darkness from whence it came, and I knew that it was dead. And as it vanished into the well, with a rending, grinding groan the ruined walls quivered from dome to base. They bent inward and buckled with a deafening reverberation, the column splintered, and with a cataclysmic crash the dome itself came thundering down. For an instant the air seemed veiled with flying debris and stone-dust, through which the tree-tops lashed madly as in a storm or an earth-quake convulsion. Then all was clear again and I stared, shaking the blood from my eyes. Where the temple had stood there lay only a colossal pile of shattered masonry and broken stones, and every column in the valley had fallen, to lie in crumbling shards.

In the silence that followed I heard Grom wailing a dirge over me. I bade him lay my sword in my hand, and he did so, and bent close to hear what I had to say, for I was passing swiftly.

"Let my tribe remember," I said, speaking slowly. "Let the tale be told from village to village, from camp to camp, from tribe to tribe, so that men may know that not man nor beast or devil may prey in safety on the golden-haired people of Asgard. Let them build me a cairn where I lie and lay me therein with my bow and sword at hand to guard this valley for ever; so if the ghost of the god I slew comes up from below, my ghost will ever be ready to give it battle."

And while Grom howled and beat his hairy breast, death came to me in the Valley of the Worm.

L. Sprague de Camp

Heldendämmerung

IN THE last story we saw how Robert E. Howard handled the classical fantasy theme of the Dragon Slayer with his usual verve and gusto and force. Here is an alternate approach via the road of parody. The deft and witty Mr. de Camp, who has posthumously collaborated with Howard on extending and completing the earlier writer's famous "Conan" saga, here displays the sharp bite of irony, the satirical humor and the adroit skills that have made him a popular master of modern swashbuckling fantasy.

This poem, incidentally, has never been published in book form until now . . . .

Hero Bigfeet, brave and brawny,
Seeks to slay the dragon Goofnir,
For he craves the golden gewgaws
Goofnir guards through endless eons.

Bigfeet bares his burnished broadsword,
Fearsome *Nothing*, forged by goblins,
Razor-sharp and rune-embellished;
Thumbs it, sheaths it, straps it to him.

170

To the garth of Goofnir goes he;
Builds a blind and lurks behind it;
Casts a stone into the cavern;
With it roars a rousing challenge:

"Come ye forth, O lazy lizard!
Come and fight, your weird to witness!"
With a Brobdingnagian bellow,
Goofnir from his sanctum shambles,

Fire from his nostrils flaring,
Left and right his leer is ranging,
For his saucy foeman searching;
'Neath his tread the earth is trembling.

Past the hero's blind he blunders.
Bigfeet hastens out from hiding,
Drawing forth his deadly *Norhing*,
Falls upon the flank of Goofnir.

But, though blade of brand is flawless—
Forged of finest fairy metal—
For the hilt, to hoard a ha'penny,
Bigfeet got a cut-rate goblin.

Hilt and blade now break asunder;
Hilt in hero's hand is brandished,
Whilst the blade, with runes bedighted,
Still abides, in scabbard sticking.

Doom of Bigfeet; dragon stated.
Back into his lair he lumbers;
Belches, bends his scaly body
Round his hoard, and sinks in slumber.

Henry Kuttner

Cursed Be the City

❖━━❖━❖━❖━❖━❖━❖━❖━❖━━❖

THERE ARE some writers you enjoy, some writers you respect, some writers you admire and some writers you whole-heartedly love. Well, I have loved Henry Kuttner since I was a kid reading *Startling Stories* in the forties, so let me tell you a little about this extraordinary and wonderfully gifted man.

Kuttner was born in Los Angeles in 1914. People who knew him personally describe him as "small, dark, shy, quiet." In his youth he worked in a literary agency, but he began writing professionally when he was hardly more than 20. Not only was he a very successful practitioner of the Loneliest Trade, but he married a gifted fellow-writer, the fantasy author C. L. Moore. They frequently worked together, under one or another name.

There seems to have been something wonderful and lovable about Kuttner. People who knew him well speak of him with an odd, gentle quaver in their voices now that he is gone from us and his typewriter is silent (Kuttner died in 1958; he was only 44). I have heard Bob Heinlein speak of him before a roomful of people, and although he began reminiscing in a quiet, controlled voice, he was soon virtually on the point of tears and had to break off and change the subject.

The man had enough sheer talent to outfit any eight ordinary wordsmiths, and his energy, his devotion to his profession, were as prodigious as the total of his publishing credits. But there are two things about Hank Kuttner I particularly respect. The first is that he refused to be typed: he was capable of producing first-rank science fiction to the taste of John Campbell, and he was good enough at it to stand out of the crowd as a distinct writing personality . . . this become more truly remarkable when you consider the extraordinary high caliber of the rest of the guys in that crowd: Heinlein, Sturgeon, Asimov, Van Vogt, L. Sprague de Camp, Leinster, Simak and L. Ron Hubbard . . . the little handful of writers who completely changed the history of science fiction in the forties, and taught it to grow up.

No, he wasn't satisfied to be just one of the better writers for *Astounding*. He wanted to write a little of everything, and to excell in each genre, and he usually did. Early in his career, he broke into *Weird Tales* with some marvellously Lovecraftian creepy-crawlies like his much-anthologized "The Graveyard Rats." And about the same time he was appearing regularly in *Astounding*, with pace-setting stuff like his "Baldy" series, and novels like *The Fairy Chessmen* and the brilliant *Fury!*, he was quietly writing a whole pile of novels for *Startling* in the vein of the lost race romance, colorful and vastly entertaining yarns much in the style of A. Merritt, novels like *The Dark World* and *I Am Eden* and *The Time Axis*.

Then again, he had a fine gift for humor, which is something very, very few science fiction writers can really do well. His delicious stories about Gallegher, the wacky inventor who could only invent when stewed to the eyelids in a welter of martinis, or the wild and wooly stories of the Hogbens, a riotous family of super-psionic hillbillies, are cases in point. Kuttner did superlatively just about everything he set his hand to, and he set his hand to just about everything.

The other thing I most respect about the man was his sense of dedication and craftsmanship. Kuttner was so highly regarded by the editors of his day that he could sell just about everything that came out of his typewriter. But to the best of my knowledge, he never skimped or cheated: every story was a polished work of fine, careful handcrafting. Every story had color and verve and charm, warmth and insight and gusto and a beautiful sense of words used well. There is hard work on every page of a Kuttner story, and I have the feeling that he worked that hard not so much out of a sense of his obligation to his readers to give them the best of which he was capable (although he certainly had that, too), but from sheer love of doing the job right. And *this* becomes all the more remarkable, when you stop to think about what it's like to be a free-lance fiction writer: if you can produce, the pay is good, but the checks don't always come in on time, and the temptation to crank out the barely adequate, collect a fast buck and ride a little on your reputation—well, it's tempting!

Kuttner's output was fantastic. He produced so much fiction that he had as many as sixteen pen-names going, and some of them, like Lewis Padgett and Lawrence O'Donnell, became well established. It becomes exciting to delve through old issues of pulp magazines, armed with a complete list of Kuttnerian pseudonyms. You turn up surprising things—did you know Kuttner was the author of *Doctor Cyclops?*

So that's Hank Kuttner, bless him! There was only one of him, and when his heart attack carried him from us, his mantle was locked away in storage: no one has yet come along with the qualifications to inherit it. When Robert E. Howard died in 1936, Henry Kuttner was one of the several writers (Mrs. Kuttner was another— remember her "Jirel of Joiry" tales?) who entered the field of Sword & Sorcery in hopes of filling the gap left empty by the passing of Conan's creator. For *Weird Tales*, Kuttner authored a series of fast action yarns about Elak of Atlantis. For *Weird Tales'* only real competitor, *Strange Stories*, Kuttner also began another fantasy adventure series about the adventures of Prince Raynor of Sardopolis, a forgotten and primal kingdom in Central Asia, set long before history began. There were only two stories in this series because *Strange* flopped on the newsstands, and Kuttner already had a series running in *WT*, so the Sardopolis mythos died before it really got started.

The two stories he did get into print, though, were very good stuff. Kuttner displays his brilliant talent for

catching the style of another writer, in this case Howard:
the Howardian flavor is unmistakable. The series showed
great promise . . . there was a haunting touch of the
poignant behind the swift moving events of the saga, and
that touch of color and poetry and fire that went into everything Kuttner handled. So, here is one of his best, for the
first time in print since April, 1939 . . . .

---

*This is the tale they tell, O King: that ere the royal banners
were lifted upon the tall towers of Chaldean Ur, before the
Winged Pharaohs reigned in secret Aegyptus, there were
mighty empires far to the east. There in that vast desert
known as the Cradle of Mankind—aye, even in the heart of
the measureless Gobi—great wars were fought and high palaces thrust their minarets up to the purple Asian sky. But
this, O King, was long ago, beyond the memory of the oldest
sage; the splendor of Imperial Gobi lives now only in the
dreams of minstrels and poets . . .*

—The Tale of Sakhmet the Damned

Chapter I
The Gates of War

IN THE gray light of the false dawn the prophet had
climbed to the outer wall of Sardopolis, his beard
streaming in the chill wind. Before him, stretching
across the broad plain, were the gay tents and pavilions
of the besieging army, emblazoned with the scarlet symbol of the wyvern, the winged dragon beneath which
King Cyaxares of the north waged his wars.

Already soldiers were grouped about the catapults
and scaling-towers, and a knot of them gathered beneath
the wall where the prophet stood. Mocking, rough

taunts were voiced, but for a time the white-bearded oldster paid no heed to the gibes. His sunken eyes, beneath their snowy penthouse brows, dwelt on the far distance, where a forest swept up into the mountain slopes and faded into blue haze.

His voice came, thin, piercing.

"Woe, woe unto Sardopolis! Fallen is the Jewel of Gobi, fallen and lost forever, and all its glory gone! Desecration shall come to the altars, and the streets shall run red with blood. I see death for the king and shame for his people . . ."

For a time the soldiers beneath the wall had been silent, but now, spears lifted, they interrupted with a torrent of half-amused mockery. A bearded giant roared:

"Come down to us, old goat! We'll welcome you indeed!"

The prophet's eyes dropped, and the shouting of the soldiers faded into stillness. Very softly the ancient spoke, yet each word was clear and distinct as a sword-blade.

"Ye shall ride through the streets of the city in triumph. And your king shall mount the silver throne. Yet from the forest shall come your doom; an old doom shall come down upon you, and none shall escape. He shall return—*He*—the mighty one who dwelt here once . . ."

The prophet lifted his arms, staring straight into the red eye of the rising sun. "*Evohé! Evohé!*"

Then he stepped forward. Two steps and plunged. Straight down, his beard and robe streaming up, till the upthrust spears caught him, and he died.

And that day the gates of Sardopolis were burst in by giant battering-rams, and like an unleashed flood the men of Cyaxares poured into the city, wolves who slew and plundered and tortured mercilessly. Terror walked that day, and a haze of battle hung upon the roofs. The defenders were hunted down and slaughtered in the streets without mercy. Women were outraged, their children impaled, and the glory of Sardopolis faded in a

smoke of shame and horror. The last glow of the setting
sun touched the scarlet wyvern of Cyaxares floating
from the tallest tower of the king's palace.

*

Flambeaux were lighted in their sockets, till the great
hall blazed with a red fire, reflected from the silver
throne where the invader sat. His black beard was all
bespattered with blood and grime, and slaves groomed
him as he sat among his men, gnawing on a mutton-
bone. Yet, despite the man's gashed and broken armor
and the filth that besmeared him, there was something
unmistakably regal about his bearing. A king's son was
Cyaxares, the last of a line that had sprung from the
dawn ages of Gobi when the feudal barons had reigned.

But his face was a tragic ruin.

Strength and power and nobility had once dwelt
there, and traces of them still could be seen, as though
in muddy water, through the mask of cruelty and vice
that lay heavy upon Cyaxares. His gray eyes held a cold
and passionless stare that vanished only in the crimson
blaze of battle, and now those deadly eyes dwelt on the
bound form of the conquered king of Sardopolis, Chalem.

In contrast with the huge figure of Cyaxares Chalem
seemed slight; yet, despite his wounds, he stood stiffly
upright, no trace of expression on his pale face.

A strange contrast! The marbled, tapestried throne-
room of the palace was more suitable to gay pageantry
than this grim scene. The only man who did not seem
incongruously out of place stood beside the throne, a
slim, dark youth, clad in silks and velvets that had apparently not been marred by the battle. This was Necho,
the king's confidant, and, some said, his familiar demon.
Whence he had come no one knew but of his evil power
over Cyaxares there was no doubt.

A little smile grew on the youth's handsome face.
Smoothing his curled dark hair, he leaned close and

whispered to the king. The latter nodded, waved away a maiden who was oiling his beard, and said shortly:

"Your power is broken, Chalem. Yet are we merciful. Render homage, and you may have your life."

For answer Chalem spat upon the marble flags at his feet.

A curious gleam came into Cyaxares' eyes. Half inaudibly he murmured, "A brave man. Too brave to die . . ."

Some impulse seemed to pull his head around until he met Necho's gaze. A message passed in that silent staring. For Cyaxares took from his side a long, blood-stained sword; he rose, stepped down from his dais—and swung the brand.

Chalem made no move to evade the blow. The steel cut through bone and brain. As the dead man fell, Cyaxares stood looking down without a trace of expression. He wrenched his sword free.

"Fling this carrion to the vultures," he commanded.

From the group of prisoners nearby came an angry oath.

The king turned to face the man who had dared to speak. He gestured.

A pair of guards pushed forward a tall, well-muscled figure, yellow-haired, with a face strong despite its youth, now darkened with rage. The man wore no armor, and his torso was criss-crossed with wounds.

"Who are you?" Cyaxares asked with ominous restraint, the sword bare in his hand.

"King Chalem's son—Prince Raynor."

"You seek death?"

Raynor shrugged. "Death has come close to me today. Slay me if you will. I've butchered about a dozen of your wolves, anyway, and that's some satisfaction."

Behind Cyaxares came a rustle of silks as Necho moved slightly. The king's lips twitched beneath the shaggy beard. His face was suddenly hard and cruel again.

"So! Well, you will crawl to my feet before the next

sun sets." He gestured. "No doubt there are torture
vaults beneath the palace. Sudrach!"

A brawny, leather-clad man stepped forward and sa-
luted. "You have heard my will. See to it."

"If I crawl to your feet," Raynor said quietly, "it'll be
to hamstring you, bloated toad."

The king drew in his breath with an angry sound.
Without another word he nodded to Sudrach, and the
torturer followed Raynor as he was conducted out. Then
Cyaxares went back to his throne and mused for a time,
till a slave brought him wine in a gilded chalice.

But the liquor had no power to break his dark mood.
At last he rose and went to the dead king's apartments,
which the invaders had not dared to plunder for fear of
Cyaxares' wrath. Above the silken couch a gleaming
image hung from its standard—the scarlet wyvern, wings
spread, barbed tail stiffly upright. Cyaxares stood silently staring at it for a space.

He did not turn when he heard Necho's soft voice.
The youth said, "The wyvern has conquered once
again."

"Aye," Cyaxares said dully. "Once again, through vile-
ness and black shame. It was an evil day when we met,
Necho."

Low laughter came. "Yet you summoned me, as I remember. I was content enough in my own place, till you
sent your summons."

Involuntarily the king shuddered. "I would Ishtar had
sent down her lightnings upon me that night."

"Ishtar? You worship another god now."

Cyaxares swung about, snarling. "Necho, do not push
me too far! I have still some power—"

"You have all power," the low voice said. "As you
wished."

For a dozen heart-beats the king made no answer.
Then he whispered, "I am the first to bring shame upon
our royal blood. When I was crowned I swore many a
vow on the tombs of my fathers—and for a time I kept
those vows. I ruled with truth and chivalry—"

"And then you sought wisdom."

"Aye. I was not content. I sought to make my name great, and to that end I talked with sorcerers—with Bleys of the Dark Pool."

"Bleys," Necho murmured. "He was learned, in his way. Yet—he died."

The king's breathing was unsteady. "I know. I slew him—at your command. And you showed me what happened thereafter."

"Bleys is not happy now," Necho said softly. "He served the same master as you. Wherefore—" The quiet voice grew imperious. "Wherefore live! For by our bargain I shall give you all power on earth, fair women and treasure beyond imagination. But when you die—you shall serve me!"

The other stood silent, while veins swelled on his swarthy forehead. Suddenly, with a bellowing, inarticulate oath, he snatched up his sword. Bright steel flamed through the air—and rebounded, clashing. Up the king's arm and through all his body raced a tingling shock, and simultaneously the regal apartment seemed to darken around him. The fires of the flambeaux darkened. The air was chill—and it whispered.

Steadily the room grew blacker. Now all was midnight black, save for a shining figure that stood immobile, blazing with weird and unearthly radiance. Little murmurs rustled through the deadly stillness. The body of Necho shone brighter, blindingly. And he stood without moving or speaking, till the king shrank with a shuddering cry, his blade clattering on the marble.

"No!" he half sobbed, "For *His* mercy—*no!*"

"*He* has no mercy," the low voice came, bleak and chill. "Therefore worship me, dog whom men call king. *Worship me!*"

And Cyaxares worshipped . . .

Chapter II
Blood in the City

Prince Raynor was acutely uncomfortable. He was stretched upon a rack, staring up at the dripping stones of the vault's roof, and Sudrach, the torturer, was heating iron bars on the hearth. A great cup of wine stood nearby, and occasionally Sudrach, humming under his breath, would reach for it and gulp noisily. "A thousand pieces of gold if you help me escape," Raynor repeated without much hope.

"What good is gold to a flayed man?" Sudrach asked. "That would be my fate if you escaped. Also, where would you get a thousand gold pieces?"

"In my apartment," Raynor said. "Safely hidden."

"You may be lying. At any rate, you'll tell me where this hiding place is when I burn out your eyes. Thus I'll have the gold—if it exists—without danger to myself."

Raynor made no answer, but instead tugged at the cords that bound him. They did not give. Yet Raynor strained until blood throbbed in his temples, and was no closer to freedom when he relaxed at last.

"You'll but wear yourself out," Sudrach said over his shoulder. "Best save your strength. You'll need it for screaming." He took an iron bar from the fire. Its end glowed redly, and Raynor watched the implement with fascinated horror. An unpleasant way to die . . .

But as the glowing bar approached Raynor's chest there came an interruption. The iron door was flung open, and a tall, huge-muscled black entered. Sudrach turned, involuntarily lifting the bar as a weapon. Then he relaxed, his eyes questioning.

"Who the devil are you?" he grunted.

"Eblik, the Nubian," said the black, bowing. "I bear a

message from the king. I lost my way in this damned palace, and just now blundered to my goal. The king has two more prisoners for your hands."

"Good!" Sudrach rubbed his hands. "Where are they?"

"In the—" The other stepped closer. He fumbled in his belt.

Then, abruptly, a blood-reddened dagger flashed up and sheathed itself in flesh. Sudrach bellowed, thrust out clawing hands. He doubled up slowly, while his attacker leaped free, and then he collapsed upon the dank stones and lay silent, twitching a little.

"The gods be praised!" Raynor grunted. "Eblik, faithful servant, you come in time!"

Eblik's dark, gargoylish face was worried. "Let me—" He slashed the cords that bound the prisoner. "It wasn't easy. When we were separated in the battle, master, I knew Sardopolis would fall. I changed clothes with one of Cyaxares' men—whom I slew—and waited my chance to escape. It was by the merest luck that I heard you had offended the king and were to be tortured. So—" He shrugged.

Raynor, free at last, sprang up from the rack, stretching his stiffened muscles. "Will it be easy to escape?"

"Perhaps. Many are drunk or asleep. At any rate, we can't stay here."

The two slipped cautiously out into the corridor. A guard lay dead, weltering in his blood, not far away. They hurried past him, and silently threaded their way through the palace, more than once dodging into passages to evade detection.

"If I knew where Cyaxares slept, I'd take my chances on slitting his throat!" Raynor said. "Wait! This way!"

At the end of a narrow hall was a door which, pushed open, showed a moonlit expanse of garden. Eblik said, "I remember—I entered this way. Here—" He dived into a bush and presently emerged with a sword and a heavy battle-ax; the latter he thrust in his girdle. "What now?"

"Over the wall," Raynor said, and led the way. The high rampart was not easy to scale, but a spreading tree grew close to it, and eventually the two had surmounted

ie barrier. As Raynor dropped lightly to the ground he
eard a sudden cry, and, glancing around, saw a group
f men, armor gleaming in the moonlight, racing toward
im. He cursed softly.

Eblik was already fleeing, his long legs covering the
ards with amazing speed. Raynor followed, though his
rst impulse was to wait and give battle. But in the
ronghold of Cyaxares such an action would have been
iicidal.

Behind the pair the pursuers bayed menace. Swords
ame out flashing. Raynor clutched his comrade's arm,
ragged him into a side alley, and the two sped on, fran-
cally searching for a hiding-place. It was Eblik who
)und sanctuary five minutes later. Passing the blood-
neared, corpse-littered courtyard of a temple, he
asped a hasty word, and in a moment both Raynor and
.blik were across the moonlit stretch and fleeing into
ie interior of the temple.

From a high roof hung a golden ball, dim in the
loom. This was the sacred house of the Sun, the dwell-
ig-place of the primal god Ahmon. Eblik had been here
efore, and knew the way. He guided Raynor past torn
apestries and overthrown censers, and then, halting be-
ore a golden curtain, he listened. There was no sound
f pursuit.

"Good!" the Nubian warrior said. "I've heard of a se-
:ret way out of here, though where it is I don't know.
Maybe we can find it."

*

Ie drew the curtain aside, and the two entered the
anctuary of the god. Involuntarily Raynor whispered a
:urse, and his brown fingers tightened on his rapier hilt.

A small chamber faced them, with walls and floor and
:eiling blue as the summer sky. It was empty, save for a
:ingle huge sphere of gold in the center.

Broken upon the gleaming ball was a man.

From the wall a single flambeau cast a flickering radi-
ince on the twisted, bloodstained body, on the white

beard that was dappled with blood. The man lay stretched across the globe, his hands and feet impaled with iron spikes that had been driven deeply into the gold.

Froth bubbled on his lips. His hoary head rolled; eyes stared unseeingly. He gasped, "Water! For the love of Ahmon, a drop of water!"

Raynor's lips were a hard white line as he sprang forward. Eblik helped him as he pried the spikes free. The tortured priest moaned and bit at his mangled lips, but made no outcry. Presently he lay prostrate on the blue floor. With a muttered word, Eblik disappeared, and came back bearing a cup which he held to the dying man's mouth.

The priest drank deeply. He whispered, "Prince Raynor! Is the King safe?"

Swiftly Raynor answered. The other's white head rolled.

"Lift me up—swiftly!"

Raynor obeyed. The priest ran his hands over the golden sphere, and suddenly, beneath the probing fingers it split in half like a cloven fruit, and in its center a gap widened. A steep staircase led down into hidden depths.

"The altar is open? I cannot see well. Take me down there. They cannot find us in the hidden chamber."

Raynor swung the priest to his shoulders and without hesitation started down the steps, Eblik behind him. There was a low grating as the altar swung back, a gleaming sphere that would halt and baffle pursuit. They were in utter darkness. The prince moved cautiously, testing each step before he shifted his weight. At last he felt the floor level beneath his feet.

Slowly, a dim light began to grow, like the first glow of dawn. It revealed a bare stone vault, roughly constructed of mortised stones, strangely at variance with the palatial city above. In one wall a dark hole showed. On the floor was a circular disk of metal, its center hollowed out into a cup. Within this cup lay a broken shard of some rock that resembled gold-shot marble, half as large as Raynor's hand. On the shard were carved certain symbols the prince did not recognize, and one that he did—the ancient looped cross, sacred to the sun-god.

He put the priest down gently, but nevertheless the man moaned in agony. The maimed hands clutched at air.

"Ahmon! Great Ahmon . . . give me more water!"

Eblik obeyed. Strengthened, the priest fumbled for and gripped Raynor's arm.

"You are strong. Good! Strength is needed for the mission you must undertake."

"Mission?"

The priest's fingers tightened. "Aye; Ahmon guided your steps hither. You must be the messenger of vengeance. Not I. I have not long to live. My strength ebbs . . ."

He was silent for a time, and then resumed. "I have a tale to tell you. Do you know the legend of the founding of Sardopolis? How, long ago, a very terrible god had his altar in this spot, and was served by all the forest dwellers . . . till those who served Ahmon came? They fought and prisoned the forest god, drove him hence to the Valley of Silence, and he lies bound there by strong magic and the seal of Ahmon. Yet there was a prophecy that one day Ahmon would be overthrown, and the bound god would break his fetters and return to his first dwelling place, to the ruin of Sardopolis. The day of the prophecy is at hand!"

The priest pointed. "All is dark. Yet the seal should be there—is it not?"

Raynor said, "A bit of marble—"

"Aye—the talisman. Lift it up!" The voice was now peremptory. Raynor obeyed.

"I have it."

"Good. Guard it well. Lift the disk now."

Almost apprehensively the prince tugged the disk up, finding it curiously light. Beneath was nothing but a jagged stone, crudely carved with archaic figures and symbols. A stone—yet Raynor knew, somehow, that the thing was horribly old, that it had existed from the dawn ages of Gobi.

"The altar of the forest god," said the priest. "He will return to this spot when he is freed. You must go to the Reaver of the Rock, and give him the talisman. He will know its meaning. So shall Ahmon be avenged upon the tyrant . . ."

Suddenly the priest surged upright, his arms lifted, tears streaming from the blind eyes. He cried, *"Ohé—ohé!* Fallen forever is the House of Ahmon! Fallen to the dust . . ."

He fell, as a tree falls, crashing down upon the stones, his arms still extended as though in worship. So died the last priest of Ahmon in Gobi.

Raynor did not move for a while. Then he bent over the lax body. A hasty examination showed him that the man was dead, and, shrugging, he thrust the marble shard into his belt.

"I suppose that's the way out," he said, pointing to the gap in the wall, "though I don't like the look of it. Well —come on."

He squeezed himself into the narrow hole, cursing softly, and Eblik followed.

Chapter III
The Reaver of the Rock

With slow steps Cyaxares paced his apartment, his shaggy brows drawn together in a frown. Once or twice his hand closed convulsively on his sword-hilt, and again the secret agony within him made him groan aloud. But not once did he glance at the scarlet symbol of the wyvern that hung above his couch.

Going over to a window, he looked down over the

city, and then his gaze went out to the plain and the distant, forested mountains. He sighed heavily.

A voice said, "You may well look there, Cyaxares. For there is your doom, unless you act swiftly."

"Is it you, Necho?" the king asked heavily. "What new shamefulness must I work now?"

"Two men go south to the Valley of Silence. They must be slain ere they reach it."

"Why? What aid can they get there?"

Necho did not answer at first. His voice was hesitant when he said, "The gods have their own secrets. There is something in the Valley of Silence that can send all your glory and power crashing down about your head. Nor can I aid you then. I can only advise you now and if you follow my advice—well. But act I cannot and must not, for a reason which you need not know. Send out your men therefore, with orders to overtake those two and slay them—swiftly!"

"As you will," the king said, and turned to summon a servitor.

*

"Soldiers follow us," Eblik said, shading his eyes with a calloused hand. He was astride a randy dun mare, and beside him Raynor rode on a great gray charger, red of nostril and fiery of eye. The latter turned in the saddle and looked back.

"By the gods!" he observed. "Cyaxares has sent half an army after us. It's lucky we managed to steal these mounts."

The two had reined their horses at the summit of a low rise in the forest. Back of them the ground sloped to the great plain and the gutted city of Sardopolis; before them jagged mountains rose, covered with oak and pine and fir. The Nubian licked dry lips, and said thirstily, "The fires of all hells are in my belly. Let's get out of this wilderness where there's nothing to drink but water."

"The Reaver may feed you wine—or blood," Raynor

said, "nevertheless, our best chance is to find this Reaver and seek his aid. A mercenary once told me of the road."

He clapped his heels against the charger's flanks, and the steed bounded forward. In a moment the ridge had hidden them from the men of Cyaxares. So the two penetrated deeper and deeper into one of the craggy, desolate wilderness, a place haunted by wolves and great bears and, men whispered, monstrous, snakelike cockadrills.

They went by snow-peaked mountains that lifted white cones to the blue sky, and they fled along the brink of deep gorges from which the low thunder of cataracts rose tumultuously. And always behind them rode the pursuers, a grim and warlike company, following slowly but relentlessly.

But Raynor used more than one stratagem. Thrice he guided his charger up streams along which the wise animal picked its way carefully; again he dislodged an avalanche to block the trail. So it came about that when the two rode down into a great, grassy basin, the men of Cyaxares were far behind.

On all sides the mountains rose. Ahead was a broad, meadow-like valley, strewn with thickets and green groves. Far ahead the precipice rose in a tall rampart, split in one place into a narrow canyon.

To the right of the gorge lifted a great gray rock, mountain-huge, bare save for a winding trail that twisted up its surface to a castle upon the summit. Dwarfed by distance, the size of the huge structure could yet be appreciated—a castle of stone, incongruously bedecked with fluttering, bright banners and pennons.

Raynor pointed. "He dwells there, The Reaver of the Rock."

"And here comes danger," Eblik said, whipping out his battle-ax. "Look!"

From a grove of nearby trees burst a company of horsemen, glittering in the afternoon sunlight, spears lifted, casques and helms agleam. Shouting, they rode down upon the waiting pair. Raynor fingered his sword-hilt, hesitating.

"Put up your blade," he directed Elbik. "We come in friendship here."

The Nubian was doubtful. "But do *they* know that?"

Nevertheless he sheathed his sword and waited till the dozen riders reined in a few paces away. One spurred forward, a tall man astride a wiry black.

"Are you tired of life, that you seek the Reaver's stronghold?" he demanded. "Or do you mean to enter in his service?"

"We bear a message," Raynor countered. "A message from a priest of Ahmon."

"We know no gods here," the other grunted.

"Well, you know warfare, or I've misread the dents in your armor," Raynor snapped. "Sardopolis is fallen! Cyaxares has taken the city and slain the king, my father, Chalem of Sardopolis."

To his amazement a bellow of laughter burst from the troop. The spokesman said, "What has that to do with us? We own no king but the Reaver. Yet you shall come safely before him, if that is your will. It were shameful to battle a dozen to two, and the rags you wear aren't worth the taking."

Eblik started like a ruffled peacock. "By the gods, you have little courtesy here! For a coin I'd slit your weasand!"

The other rubbed his throat reflectively, grinning. "You may have a trial at that later, if you wish, my ragged gargoyle. But come, now, for the Reaver is in hall, and tonight he rides forth on a raid."

With a nod, Raynor spurred his horse forward, the Nubian at his side, and, surrounded by the men of the Reaver, they fled across the valley toward the castle. Thence they mounted the steep, dangerous path up the craggy ramp, till at last they crossed a drawbridge and dismounted in a courtyard.

So they took Raynor before the Reaver of the Rock.

A great, shining, red-cheeked man he was, with a grizzled gray beard and a crown set rakishly askew on tangled locks. He sat before a blazing fire in a high-roofed stone hall, an iron chest open at his feet. From this he was taking jewels and golden chains and ornaments that might have graced a king's treasury, examining them carefully, and making notes with a quill pen upon a parchment on his lap.

He looked up; merry eyes dwelt on Raynor's flushed face and tousled yellow hair.

"Well, Samar, what is it now?"

"Two strangers. They have a message for you—or so they say."

Suddenly the Reaver's face changed. He leaned forward, spilling treasure from his lap. "A message? Now there is only one message that can ever come to me . . . speak, you! Who sent you?"

Raynor stepped forward confidently. From his belt he drew the broken shard of marble, and extended it.

"A priest of Ahmon bade me give you this," he said. "Sardopolis is fallen."

For a heartbeat there was silence. Then the Reaver took the shard, examining it carefully. He murmured, "Aye. So my rule passes. For long and long my fathers held the Rock, waiting for the summons that never came. And now it has come."

He looked up. "Go, all of you, save you two. And you, Samar—wait, for you should know of this."

The others departed. The Reaver shouted after them, "Summon Delphia!"

He turned to stare into the fire. "So I, Kialeh, must fulfill the ancient pledge of my ancestors. And invaders are on my marches. Well—"

There came an interruption. A girl strode in, dark head proudly erect, slim figure corseted in dinted armor. She went to the Reaver, flung a blazing jewel in his lap.

"Is this my guerdon?" she snarled. "Faith o' the gods, I took Ossan's castle almost single-handed. And my share is less than the share of Samar here!"

"You are my daughter," the Reaver said quietly. "Shall

I give you more honor, then, in our free brotherhood?
Be silent. Listen."

Raynor was examining the girl's face with approval.
There was beauty there, wild dark lawless beauty, and
strength that showed in the firm set of the jaw and the
latent fire of the jet eyes. Ebony hair, unbound, fell in
ringlets about steel-corseleted shoulders.

The girl said, "Well? Have you had your fill of staring?"

"Let be," the Reaver grunted. "I have a tale for all of
you . . . listen."

His deep voice grew stronger. "Ages on ages ago this
was a barbarous land. The people worshipped a forest-
god called—" his hand moved in a queer quick sign—
"called Pan. Then from the north came two kings, brothers, bringing with them the power of the sun-god,
Ahmon. There was battle in the land then, and blood
and reddened steel. Yet Ahmon conquered.

"The forest-god was bound within the Valley of Silence, which lies beyond my castle. The two kings made
an agreement. One was to rule Sardopolis, and the
other, the younger, was to rear a great castle at the gateway of the Valley of Silence, and guard the fettered god.
Until a certain word should come . . ."

The Reaver weighed a glittering stone in his hand.
"For there was a prophecy that one day the rule of
Ahmon should be broken. Then it was foretold that the
forest-god should be freed, and should bring vengeance
upon the destroyers of Sardopolis. For long and long my
ancestors have guarded the Rock—and I, Kialeh, am the
last. Ah," he sighed. "The great days are over indeed.
Never again will the Reaver ride to rob and plunder and
mock at gods. Never—what's this?"

A man-at-arms had burst into the hall, eyes alight,
face fierce as a wolf's. "Kialeh! An army is in the valley!"

"By Shaitan!" Raynor cursed. "Cyaxares' men! They
pursued us—"

The girl, Delphia, swung about. "Gather the men! I'll
take command—"

Suddenly the Reaver let out a roaring shout. "No! By all the gods I've flouted—*no!* Would you grudge me my last battle, girl? Gather your men, Samar—but *I* command!"

Samar sprang to obey. Delphia gripped her father's arm. "I fight *with* you, then."

"I have another task for you. Guide these two through the Valley of Silence, to the place you know. Here—" he thrust the marble shard at the prince. "Take this. You'll know how to use it when the time comes."

Then he was gone, and curtains of black samite swayed into place behind him.

Raynor was curiously eying the girl. Her face was pale beneath its tan, and her eyes betrayed fear. Red battle she could face unflinchingly, but the thought of entering the Valley of Silence meant to her something far more terrible. Yet she said, "Come. We have little time."

Eblik followed Raynor and Delphia from the hall. They went through the harsh splendor of the castle, till at last the girl halted before a blank stone wall. She pressed a hidden spring. A section of the rock swung away, revealing the dim-lit depths of a passage.

Delphia paused on the threshold. Her dark eyes flickered over the two.

"Hold fast to your courage," she whispered—and her lips were trembling. "For now we go down into Hell . . ."

Chapter IV

The Valley of Silence

Yet at first there seemed nothing terrible about the valley. They entered it from a cavern that opened on thick forest, and, glancing around, Raynor saw ta

mountainous ramparts that made the place a prison indeed. It was past sunset, yet already a full moon was rising over the eastern cliffs, outlining the Reaver's castle
in black silhouette.

They entered the forest.

Moss underfoot deadened their footsteps. They
walked in dim gloom, broken by moonlight traceries fil-
tered through the leaves. And now Raynor noted the curious stillness that hung over all.

There was no sound. The noise of birds and beasts did
not exist here, nor did the breath of wind rustle the silent trees. But, queerly, the prince thought there *was* a
sound whispering through the forest, a sound below the
threshold of hearing, which nevertheless played on his
taut nerves.

"I don't like this," Eblik said, his ugly face set and
strained. His voice seemed to die away with uncanny
swiftness.

"Pan is fettered here," Delphia whispered. "Yet is his
power manifest . . ."

Soundlessly they went through the soundless forest.
And now Raynor realized that, slowly and impercepti-
bly, the shadowy whisper he had sensed was growing
louder—or else his ears were becoming more attuned to
it. A very dim murmur, faint and far away, which yet
seemed to have within it a multitude of voices . . .

The voices of the winds . . . the murmur of forests
. . . the goblin laughter of shadowed brooks . . .

It was louder now, and Raynor found himself thinking
of all the innumerable sounds of the primeval wilderness. Bird-notes, and the call of beasts . . .

And under all, a dim, powerful motif, beat a wordless
shrilling, a faint piping that set the prince's skin to
crawling as he heard it.

"It is the tide of life," Delphia said softly. "The heartbeat of the first god. The pulse of earth."

For the first time Raynor felt something of the primal
secrets of the world. Often he had walked alone in the
forest, but never yet had the hidden heart of the wilderness reached fingers into his soul. He sensed a mighty

and very terrible power stirring latent in the soil beneath him, a thing bound inextricably to the brain of man by the cords of the flesh which came up, by slow degrees, from the seething ocean which once rolled unchecked over a young planet. Unimaginable eons ago man had come from the earth and the brand of his mother-world was burned deep within his soul.

Afraid, yet strangely happy, as men are sometimes happy in their dreams, the prince motioned for his companions to increase their pace.

The forest gave place to a wide clearing, with shattered white stones rearing to the sky. Broken plinths and peristyles gleamed in the moonlight. A temple had once existed here. Now all was overgrown with moss and the slow-creeping lichen.

"Here," the girl said in a low whisper. "Here . . ."

In the center of a ring of fallen pillars they halted. Delphia pointed to a block of marble, on which a metal disk was inset. In a cuplike depression in the metal lay a broken bit of marble.

"The talisman," Delphia said. "Touch it to the other."

Silence . . . and the unearthly tide of hidden life swelling and ebbing all about them. Raynor took the amulet from his belt, stepped forward, fighting down his fear. He bent above the disk—touched marble shard to marble—

As iron to lodestone, the two fragments drew together. They coalesced into one. The jagged line of breakage faded and vanished.

Raynor held the talisman—complete, unbroken!

Now, quite suddenly, the vague murmurings mounted into a roar—gay, jubilant, triumphant! The metal disk shattered into fragments. Beneath it the prince glimpsed a small carved stone, the twin of the one beneath the temple of Ahmon.

Above the unceasing roar sounded a penetrating shrill piping.

Delphia clutched at Raynor's arm, pulling him back. Her face was chalk-white.

"The pipes!" she gasped. "Back—quickly! To see Pan is to die!"

Louder the roar mounted, and louder. In its bellow was a deep shout of alien laughter, a thunder of goblin merriment. The chuckle of shadowed brooks was the crash of cataracts and waterfalls.

The forest stirred to a breath of gusty wind.

"Back!" the girl said urgently. "Back! We have freed Pan!"

Without conscious thought Raynor thrust the talisman into his belt, turned, and, with Delphia and Eblik beside him, fled into the moonlit shadows. Above him branches tossed in a mounting wind. The wild shrieking of the pipes grew louder.

The tide of earth life—rising to a mad paean of triumph!

The wind exulted:

"Free . . . free!"

And the unseen rovers shouted:

"Great Pan is free!"

*

Clattering of hoofs came from the distance. Bleating calls sounded from afar.

The girl stumbled, almost fell. Raynor gripped her arm, pulling her upright, fighting the unreasoning terror that mounted within him. The Nubian's grim face was glistening with sweat.

"Pan, Pan is free!"

"Evohé!"

The black mouth of a cavern loomed before them. At its threshold Raynor cast a glance behind him, saw all the great forest swaying and tossing. His breath coming unevenly, he turned, following his companions into the cave.

"Shaitan!" he whispered. "What demon have I loosed on the land?"

Then it was race, sprint, pound up the winding passage, up an unending flight of stone steps, through a wall that lifted at Delphia's touch—and into a castle shaking with battle. Raynor stopped short, whipping out his sword, staring at shadows flickering in the distance.

"Cyaxares' men," he said. "They've entered."

In the face of flesh-and-blood antagonists, the prince was suddenly himself again. Delphia was already running down the corridor, blade out. Raynor and the Nubian followed.

They burst into the great hall. A ring of armed men surrounded a little group who were making their last stand before the hearth. Towering above the others Raynor saw the tangled locks and bristling beard of Kialeh, the Reaver, and beside him his lieutenant Samar. Corpses littered the floor.

"Ho!" roared the Reaver, as he caught sight of the newcomers. "You come in time! In time—to die with us!"

Chapter V
Cursed Be the City

Grim laughter touched Raynor's lips. He drove in, sheathing his sword in a brawny throat, whipped it out, steel singing. Nor were Eblik and Delphia far behind. Her blade and the Nubian's ax wreaked deadly havoc among Cyaxares' soldiers, who, not expecting attack from the rear, were confused.

The hall became filled with a milling, yelling throng, from which one soldier, a burly giant, emerged, shouting down the others.

"Cut them down! They're but three!"

Then all semblance of sanity was lost in a blaze of crimson battle, swinging brands, and huge maces that crashed down, splitting skulls and spattering gray brain-stuff. Delphia kept shoulder to shoulder with Ray-

nor, seemingly heedless of danger, her blade flicking
wasplike through the air. And the prince guarded her as
best he could, the sword weaving a bright maze of
deadly lightnings as it whirled.

The Reaver swung, and his sword crushed a helm and
bit deep into bone. He strained to tug it free—and a soldier thrust up at his throat. Samar deflected the blade
with his own weapon, and that cost him his life. In that
moment of inattention a driven spear smashed through
corselet and jerkin and drank deep of the man's life-
blood.

Silent, he fell.

The Reaver went berserk. Yelling, he sprang over his
lieutenant's corpse and swung. For a few moments he
held back his enemies—and then someone flung a shield.
Instinctively Kialeh lifted his blade to parry.

The wolves leaped in to the kill.

Roaring, the Reaver went down, blood gushing
through his shaggy beard, staining its iron-gray with
red. When Raynor had time to look again, Kialeh lay a
corpse on his own hearth, his head amid bright jewels
that had spilled from the overturned treasure-chest.

The three stood together now, the last of the defenders—Raynor and Eblik and Delphia. The soldiers ringed
them, panting for their death, yet hesitating before the
menace of cold steel. None wished to be the first to die.

And, as they waited, a little silence fell. The prince
heard a sound he remembered.

Dim and far away, a low roaring drifted to his ears.
And the eerie shrilling of pipes . . .

It grew louder. The soldiers heard it now. They
glanced at one another askance. There was something
about that sound that chilled the blood.

It swelled to a gleeful shouting, filling all the castle. A
breeze blew through the hall, tugging with elfin fingers
at sweat-moist skin. It rose to a gusty blast.

In its murmur voices whispered.

"Evohé! Evohé!"

They grew louder, mad and unchecked. They exulted.

"Pan, Pan is free!"

"Gods!" a soldier cursed. "What devil's work is this?" He swung about, sword ready.

The curtains of samite were ripped away by the shrieking wind. Deafeningly the voices exulted:

"Pan is free!"

The piping shrilled out. There came the chatter of ringing little hoofs. The castle rocked and shuddered.

Some vague, indefinable impulse made Raynor snatch at his belt, gripping the sun-god's talisman in bronzed fingers. From it a grateful warmth seemed to flow into his flesh—and the roaring faded.

He dragged Delphia and the Nubian behind him. "Close to me! Stay close!"

The room was darkening. No—it seemed as though a cloudy veil of mist dropped before the three, guarding them. Raynor lifted the seal of Ahmon.

The fog-veils swirled. Dimly through them Raynor could see the soldiers moving swiftly, frantically, like rats caught in a trap. He tightened one arm about Delphia's steel-armored waist.

Suddenly the hall was ice-cold. The castle shook as though gripped by Titan hands. The floor swayed beneath the prince's feet.

The mists darkened. Through rifts he saw half-guessed figures that leaped and bounded . . . heard elfin hoofs clicking. Horned and shaggy-furred beings that cried jubilantly as they danced to the pipes of Pan . . .

Faun and dryad and satyr swung in a mad saraband beyond the shrouding mists. Faintly there came the screaming of men, half drowned in the loud shrilling.

"Evohé!" the demoniac rout thundered. *"Evohé!* All hail, O Pan!"

With a queer certainty, Raynor knew that it was time to leave the castle—and swiftly. Already the great stone structure was shaking like a tree in a hurricane. With a word to his companions he stepped forward hesitantly, the talisman held high.

The walls of mist moved with him. Outside the fog-walls the monstrous figures gamboled. But the soldiers of Cyaxares screamed no more.

Through a castle toppling into ruin the three sped, into the courtyard, across the drawbridge, and down the face of the Rock. Nor did they pause till they were safely in the broad plain of the valley.

"The castle!" Eblik barked, pointing. "See? It falls."

And it was true. Down it came thundering, while clouds of ruin spurted up. Then there was only a shattered wreck on the summit of the Rock . . .

Delphia caught her breath in a little sob. She murmured, "The end of the Reavers for all time. I—I lived in the castle for more than twenty years. And now it's gone like a puff of dust before the wind."

The walls of fog had vanished. Raynor returned the talisman to his belt. Eblik, staring up at the Rock, swallowed uneasily.

"Well, what now?" he asked.

"Back along the way we came," the prince said. "It's the only way out of this wilderness that I know of."

The girl nodded. "Yes. Beyond the mountains lie deserts, save towards Sardopolis. But we have no mounts."

"Then we'll walk," Eblik observed, but Raynor caught his arm and pointed.

"There! Horses—probably stampeded from the castle. And—Shaitan! There's my gray charger. Good!"

So, presently, the three rode towards Sardopolis, conscious of a weird dim throbbing that seemed to pulse in the air all about them.

*

At dawn they topped a ridge and saw before them the plain. All three reined in their mounts, staring. Beneath them lay the city—but changed!

It was a ruin.

Doom had come to Sardopolis in the night. The mighty towers and battlements had fallen, and huge gaps were opened in the walls. Of the king's palace nothing was left but a single tower, from which, ironically, the wyvern banner flew. As they watched, that pinnacle, too, swayed and tottered and fell, and the scarlet wyvern drifted down into the dust of Sardopolis.

On fallen towers and peristyles distant figures moved, with odd, ungainly boundings. Quickly Raynor turned his eyes away. But he could not shut his ears to the distant crying of pipes, gay and pagan, yet with a faintly mournful undertone.

"Pan has returned to his first altar," Delphia said quietly. "We had best not loiter here."

"By all hell, I agree," the Nubian grunted, digging his heels into his steed's flanks. "Where now, Raynor?"

"Westwards, I think, to the Sea of Shadows. There are cities on its shore, and galleys to take us to a haven. Unless—" He turned questioning eyes on Delphia.

She laughed, a little bitterly. "I cannot stay here. The land is sunk back into the pit. Pan rules. I go with you."

The three rode to the west. They skirted, but did not enter, a small grove where a man lay in agony. It was Cyaxares, a figure so dreadfully mangled that only sheer will kept him alive. His face was a bloody mask. The once-rich garments were tattered and filthy. He saw the three riders, and raised his voice in a weak cry which the wind drowned.

Beside the king a slim, youthful figure lounged, leaning idly against an oak-trunk. It was Necho.

"Call louder, Cyaxares," he said. "With a horse under you, you can reach the Sea of Shadows. And if you succeed in doing that, you will yet live for many years."

Again the king cried out. The wind took his voice and shredded it to impotent fragments.

Necho laughed softly. "Too late, now. They are gone."

Cyaxares let his battered head drop, his beard trailing in the dirt. Through shredded lips he muttered, "If I reach the Sea of Shadows . . . I live."

"True. But if you do not, you die. And then—" Low laughter shook the other.

Groaning, the king dragged himself forward. Necho followed.

"A good horse can reach the Sea of Shadows in three

days. If you walk swiftly, you may reach it in six. But you must hurry. Why do you not rise, my Cyaxares?"

"The king spat out bitter oaths. In agony he pulled himself forward, leaving a trail of blood on the grass . . . blood that dripped unceasingly from the twin raw stumps just above his ankles.

"The stone that fell upon you was sharp, Cyaxares, was it not?" Necho mocked. "But hurry! You have little time. There are mountains to climb and rivers to cross . . ."

So, in the trail of Raynor and Eblik and Delphia, crept the dying king, hearing fainter and ever fainter the triumphant pipes of Pan from Sardopolis. And presently, patient as the silent Necho, a vulture dipped against the blue and took up the pursuit, the beat of its wings distinctly audible in the heavy, stagnant silence . . .

And Raynor and Delphia and Eblik rode onward towards the sea . . .

Ka the Appalling

THUS the late Henry Kuttner handled the heroic tale laid in an ancient, mythic age with his usual sense of gusto, color and verve. But not with any particular degree of originality, it must be observed. There is little difference between the style and substance of "Cursed Be the City" and any of Robert E. Howard's "Conan" stories, which Kuttner was obviously emulating.

Our next author, however, is very much his own man.

L. Sprague de Camp was born in New York in 1907, graduated from the California Institute of Technology with a Bachelor of Science degree in aeronautical engineering, continued his studies at the graduate school of the Massachusetts Institute of Technology, and received his M.S. degree in 1933 from Stevens Institute of Technology in New Jersey. Although he entered a full time career as a fiction writer only five years after this, all that technical training did not go to waste for his early work was in science fiction written under the exacting eye of John W. Campbell, Jr., in *Astounding Science Fiction*. He soon found fantasy more to his taste, and began producing some of the best and most significant imaginative fiction of the 1940's, much of it written in collaboration with Fletcher Pratt: books like *Land of Unreason*, *The Incomplete Enchanter*, *The Castle of Iron* and many others. He has since gone on to the writing of excellent historical novels like *An Elephant for Aristotle*, and *The Dragon of the Ishtar Gate*, and a number of books on the history of science such as *The Heroic Age of American Invention* and *The Ancient Engineers*. Most recently he has served the cause of fantasy brilliantly by editing the complete "Conan" saga for paperback publication, completing a number of stories left unfinished at Robert E. Howard's death and writing a number of Conanesque pastiches with Bjorn Nyberg and myself to fill in the more prominent gaps in Howard's original saga. He now lives in a suburb of Philadelphia with his charming blond wife, Catherine, and the younger of his two sons. When he is not globe-trotting in Yucatan, sailing up the Nile or exploring the ruins of Carthage to gather factual data for forthcoming books, that is.

Although one of his best non-fiction books is a lengthy, scholarly and devastating debunking of the historical reality of Atlantis (*Lost Continents: The Atlantis Theme in History, Science, and Literature*, Gnome Press, 1954), L. Sprague de Camp is no more immune to the tempting lure of the Atlantis legend than any other author.

Here, in a pleasing counterpoint to Kuttnerian derring-do, is one of de Camp's "Pusâdian" tales, laid not in Atlantis but in its world. He calls the lost land "Pusâd," by the way, pretending the Greeks derived their term "Poseidonis," an alternate name for Atlantis, from this source. Where Henry Kuttner saw Shamballah through the rosy spectacles of the romantic swashbuckler, de Camp views his elder and mythic civilization with the clear vision of one who knows the ancient world was not all glistening marble and snowy togas.

Among other elements, his story makes the amusing point that whatever the epoch or however glamorous and exotic the locale, men act pretty much the same today as yesterday. With his customary dry wit and aplomb, then, here is de Camp's wry, amusingly anti-glamorized tale of a businesslike thief of tomb-treasure, his nubile and not-unamenable daughter, a foxy familiar, a practical-minded hero and a no-nonsense god . . . .

As he ran through the streets of Typhon, Gezun of Gadaira recalled the words of the Ausonian adept whom he had met in Maxia:

"Typhon rises in black and purple from the mystic margins of the Sea of Thesh, amid the towering tombs of kings who reigned in splendor over Setesh when mighty Torrutseish was but a village and golden Kernê but an empty stretch of beach. No man knows the total tale of Typhon's history, or the convolutions of its streets and secret passages, or the hoarded treasures of its kings, or the hidden powers of its wizards . . ."

Just now, Gezun would gladly have given the hoarded treasures of the Seteshan kings to be carried far from this accursed place. For a youth of nineteen, he had seen much since slavers had stolen him from his home in windy Lorsk in Pusâd, or Poseidonis as the Hesperians called it. But he had never seen a city where people tried to tear a man to bits for killing a cat.

He rounded a corner as stones whizzed past him. If there had been only a few Typhonians, he would not have fled. As it was, he had laid out two with his staff before the throng had become too many to handle, even though he was nearly twice their size.

For the Seteshans were a small people, dark, slender, hatchet-faced, and scant of beard, while Gezun was a typical Lorska: over six feet before he had reached his full growth, with the bold rugged features, the big sharp nose, beetling brow, and square jutting jaw of his folk. His skin was almost as dark as a Seteshan's. His hair was thick, black, and curly, and he had a respectable beard despite his youth. A girl in Yavan had told him he looked like a god—not the grim sort of god who broods on people's sins and dispenses doom by thunderbolts, but the kind who roams the earth teaching people to make wine and looking for likely mortal maids on whom to get demigods.

In the open, he could have outrun most Seteshans. In these twisted streets, however, he hesitated at turnings long enough to let the mob gain back what they had lost in the straight stretches.

Furthermore, with such a large crowd, there were bound to be some swift runners. These pressed to the front. Their teeth gleamed, their eyes glared, and foam blew back from their chins. They bore knives, stones, bricks—whatever they had snatched up. Their panting breaths were like the hissing of a thousand snakes.

Gezun passed a tavern where a pair of King Zeremab'a archers lounged in the doorway. He slid to a stop and pointed back at the mob.

"They—look—help me—" he gasped.

The soldiers glanced. The mob shrieked: "Slay the cat-killer! Burn the blasphemer! Flay the foul foreigner!"

The soldiers looked at one another. One cried: "Slay the foreign devil!" and drew his dagger.

Gezun hit him over the ear with his staff and knocked him sprawling. The other archer started forward but fell over his companion. Gezun ran on, a corner of his cloak flapping behind him like a flag.

Passing a potter's stall, he jerked the rack of finished pots so that it fell forward with a crash, filling the street with bouncing, rolling, and smashing pots. The obstacle hardly checked the mob. The leaders cleared the pots in long leaps. The rest flowed over them like some natural force. A few fell, but the rest trampled on and scrambled over the fallen, heedless of what bones of their own folk they broke if they could only get at the hated alien.

Another corner. Gezun's teeth showed, too, as he gasped. His staff got heavier with every stride. Should he throw it away or keep it for his last stand? He had a short bronze Tartessian sword under his cloak, but with the staff he might be able to hold the mob at arm's length. The sword, though deadlier, would let them close enough to fasten on him like the giant leeches of the Tritonian Sea and pull him down.

With a burst of speed, Gezun gained enough so that he turned one corner before the mob rounded the last one. Coming out upon a street in which Gezun was not to be seen, the mob hesitated before dividing like a stream of ants, half going each way.

Gezun made another turn, into a mere alley, not wide enough to let two men pass unless they sidled past one another. It was so crooked he could see along it only a few paces. On either side rose high walls of stone or brick, without openings save once in a while a stout wooden door. Gezun knew enough of Seteshan customs not to expect help there.

The alley ended. Gezun faced another wall across his path. He was in a cul-de-sac. The walls rose smoothly around him, save where to one side there was a gap a pace wide between two houses.

The space was blocked up to the height of a man by a mass of rubble from some earlier edifice, which had been simply pushed into the place between the houses when they were built. A man could climb over the fallen masonry. Beyond it, however, rose the wall of still another house. So the space between the houses formed a minor cul-de-sac, branching off from the main one.

The sound of the mob, muted for the moment, rose again. Plainly, they were coming down the alley to see if he had taken refuge there. The crowd had put off an offshoot, like a tendril, to probe all nearby cavities for its prey.

In such a narrow space they could come at him only one or two at a time. If they were mere soldiers, he might hold them off, at least until he dropped from exhaustion or somebody fetched a bow to shoot him. But, with a mob of fanatics, those behind would push those in front, willing or not, up against Gezun faster than he could knock or cut them down.

The end would be the same, with the swarm fastening on him, using teeth and nails if there was no room to wield a weapon. Teeth and nails would kill one just as dead as swords and spears, and rather more painfully.

Gezun pounded on the nearest door. The copper shutter that closed the peep-hole on the inside moved aside. A black Seteshan eye looked out.

"Let me in," said Gezun. "I am beset."

The shutter moved back into place. Gezun angrily thrust at it with his staff, but it held. He was not surprised. The noise of the mob grew louder.

The pile of rubble might make a better place for a last stand than the alley proper. Not only was the gap between the houses narrower, but also, by mounting the pile, one could make the pursuers climb up and whack them on the sconce as they came.

Gezun sprang into the gap and had begun to climb the pile when a voice said: "In here, foreign devil!"

Between the pile of rubble and the wall of the right-hand house, an opening had appeared. A face, obscured by the deep shadow, looked up.

"Hasten!" said the face.

The crowd-noises sounded as if they were just around the next bend. Gezun lowered his large feet into the hole and squeezed through. His feet found a dirt floor.

"Out of the way, fool!" said the face.

The owner of the face pushed Bezun aside and thrust a piece of old rotten wood into the opening. It cut off most of the light. Since the fit was not tight, some light came into the tunnel around the wood. The tunnel itself was not utterly dark. A flickering light came around the first bend.

"Come," said the man.

He was a small brown Seteshan in a long dirty robe. He had sharp irregular features and crooked teeth. He was bald save for gray tufts that stood out over each ear.

The man led the way down the tunnel, muttering: "Hurry, barbarian clod! They may poke around and find my tunnel. And watch your head."

The last advice was too late; Gezun had just hit his forehead on a cross-beam. The tunnel had been built for Seteshans, not towering Pusadians. The roof had been shored up by odd bits of timber, so that to walk through the tunnel one had to duck and dodge with every step.

Gezun followed, bent over, his head ringing. He still gasped from his run; his tunic was sweat-soaked.

Around the corner, a Seteshan girl held a rushlight.

She walked ahead of the two men, shielding the light with her hand. The tunnel bent this way and that but seemed to go deeper. The soil, powder-dry near the surface, became moist as they went down. The blistering heat of the Seteshan summer gave way to delicious coolth.

The tunnel branched and forked. Gezun tried to remember his turnings but soon gave up.

The tunnel became a regular structure of dressed stone, as if they had reached the crypt of some large building. They halted where the tunnel opened out into a series of rooms.

The girl lit two more rushlights. Gezun saw that she was handsome in a slender birdlike way, though she looked a little like the man. Like him she had blue-black hair and olive-brown skin.

"Sit," said the man.

Gezun sank down on a bench and threw off his cloak. He sat holding his head and drinking in the cool air. He sneezed, wiped the drying sweat from his face with a corner of his cloak, and said:

"How came you to save me?"

"I saw the start of the chase," said the man. "I went into my tunnels and later heard the sounds of the mob near another of my entrances. You must have circled round and nearly returned to your starting-place."

"I don't know Typhon well."

"So I see. Who are you?"

"Gezun of Gadaira."

"Where is that?"

"Far to the west. I was born in Poseidonis."

"Of that I have heard; a sinking land in the sea."

"Who are you, sir?"

"Ugaph the son of Shepsaa. This is my daughter Ro. What do you so far from home?"

"I like to wander. I make a living as a wizard."

"*You* a wizard? Ha!"

"I was a pupil of the great Sacheth Sar."

"I never heard of him. If he was not a Seteshan, he cannot have amounted to much."

Gezun shrugged. "I let my clients praise me."

"When got you here?"

"Yesterday. I was strolling about, minding my own business—"

"Slowly, or I cannot understand. You speak our tongue barbarously."

"I was minding my own business and enjoying the sights of the city when your people tried to kill me."

"What led you to do so mad a thing as to slay a cat?"

"I bought a loaf and a fish in the agora for my dinner. Then I went to a tavern by the side of the agora. I bought a mug of barley-beer, and the taverner cooked my fish. I had my dinner laid out on the table outside the tavern and had just turned my head to look at a pretty girl, when this wretched cat leaped to the table and made off with my fish. I struck it with my staff and killed it, and was scraping the dirt off my fish when the mob began screaming and throwing things. By Lyr's barnacles, why?"

"Cats are sacred to Shekhemet. Since nobody hinders them, they take what they like."

"Why don't you kill me, then?"

Ugaph chuckled. "I have no love for the official cults. Priests magnify the powers of their gods to awe their dupes. Often I doubt if gods exist."

"Really? I knew a philosopher in Gadaira who said there were no gods or spirits, but I've known too many supernatural beings for such an extreme view."

Ugaph waved a hand. "Oh, spirits exist. In fact I, who dabble in magic, have my own familiar. But as for gods —well, there are all sorts of theories. Some say they are created by people's belief in them."

"Then let's be careful not to believe in them, lest they get power over us. But what of my fate?"

"I can use you, young man."

"For what?" asked Gezun.

"Have you ever hunted bats?"

"No. Why should anybody hunt bats?"

"I have use for them. My daughter has been getting them for me while I went about my business."

"What business is that?"

"I am a collector. As I was saying, Ro has been getting my bats, but I need her help in my business. Moreover, she is likelier to catch a rich husband in the city than prowling dusty tombs."

"I see."

"Furthermore, other members of my profession sometimes try to take from me the part of these tunnels I have marked out for my own, and I need a strong arm and a keen blade to drive them out. So, if you will serve as my apprentice, I will hide you, disguise you, and protect you from the superstitious mob."

"Will you also feed me and replace my garments when they wear out?"

"Surely, surely."

"Then let's begin. I was hungry when the mob drove me from my dinner, and now I'm ravenous."

Ugaph wrinkled his nose. "You are not backward. Ro, get Gezun something to eat."

The girl went into the adjoining chamber. Gezun said: "I know not how you can call collecting a business. I've heard of people who spent trade-metal that way, but never of anybody who made it."

"That is simple. I am a benefactor of the people of Typhon."

"Oh?"

"You see, the temples are full of loot of which the priests have fleeced the folk by playing on their fears. I recover this stolen wealth and put it back into circulation. Like this."

Ugaph showed a handful of gold, silver, and gems. The pieces of metal seemed to have been broken or cut from larger structures.

Gezun looked at the man with more respect. Of all thieves, the temple-thief needed the most nerve, because of what the priests did if they caught him. The priests of Typhon, especially, were known for the ingenuity of their human sacrifices. Ro came in with a plate of food.

"Thank you, beautiful," said Gezun.

Ugaph said: "Cast no lustful eyes thither, Master

Gezun. A daughter of Setesh mates not with foreign devils. It were both immoral and unlawful. Nor think to lout me behind my back, for I have magical powers. I shall watch your every move from afar."

"So?" said Gezun, stuffing his mouth.

*

Next morning Gezun went to the public stables, where he had left his ass, to get his belongings. Ugaph had fitted him out to look like a Seteshan. Like other commoners of Typhon, he wore only sandals and a linen kilt. His whole head and face had been shaved, save for a short braided scalp-lock behind and a narrow little goatee on his chin. He had left his sword and staff in the tunnels, the former because commoners were not allowed to carry them, the latter because it might help some member of yesterday's mob to recognize him.

When he had gotten back his gear and paid for fodder for his ass, Gezun rejoined Ugaph and his daughter. Ugaph said: "I will take your bags to our quarters while Ro shows you how to catch bats."

Gezun hesitated about giving up his bags, but Ro would serve as hostage for them. Ro carried two bags herself, one empty and the other containing food and rushlights.

"I see your tribe of barbarians spoils its women," said Ugaph. "Farewell."

Ro led Gezun west, away from the waterfront, picking the way through the maze of crooked streets. Typhon, Gezun thought, stank even worse than Torrutseish. After an hour's walk they passed through a gate in the wall.

Beyond the wall, the city thinned out to suburbs. Beyond the suburbs lay fields criss-crossed by irrigation-ditches. Beyond the fields, on the skyline, lines of squat, bulky structures rose from the desert sands. Gezun had seen these on his way to Typhon.

"What are those?" he asked.

"The tombs of our kings," said Ro.

Some of the structures were true pyramids, some truncated pyramids, some stepped pyramids. The tallest of the true pyramids towered hundreds of feet high. Some were new, surrounded by complexes of walls, courts, and temples; others were old, with the complexes robbed of their stones and the pyramids themselves crumbling at the edges.

As they neared the tombs, Gezun noticed that the newer ones seemed manned. Soldiers walked the walls of the complexes, and he glimpsed priests in the courtyards.

"Who are those people?" he asked.

"The attendants of the kings of this dynasty, the ancestors of King Zeremab, on whom be life, health, and strength."

"What about the older tombs, those that seem to be falling down?"

"King Zeremab cares nought for the ghosts of kings of former dynasties. So their tombs have all been plundered and lie open to us."

"Is that where we're going?"

"Aye. I thought we should try the tomb of King Khephru. It has many passages where bats seek refuge during the day."

"Now what in the seven hells does your father want bats for?"

Ro smiled. "His familiar has a taste for bats' blood."

"You mean a familiar demon?"

"Aye, Tety. Here is Khephru's tomb."

She led him into the ruined courtyard, where the sand covered most of the pavement and half-buried such statues as remained. The original entrance to the pyramid had been plugged by blocks of granite, but spoilers had bored through the softer limestone around the granite.

"Watch your step," said Ro, leaping up the first few tiers of stone. "Are you good at making fire?"

"None better."

Gezun got out his tinder-box and fire-stones. In a quarter-hour, he had a rushlight lit. Ro led him into the passage, which sloped down and forked. By the light of the rush-candle, Gezun saw more forks.

"By the beard of Roi! This place is like a rabbit-warren," he said.

"Not so loud; you will frighten the bats."

They crept along, talking in whispers. Presently Ro pointed to a little black blob on the roof of the passage. She stole up and snatched it. The bat fluttered and squeaked in her grasp, but she popped it into the bag.

"Now you try," she said.

Gezun missed his first snatch; the awakened bat whirred off into the darkness. There was a chorus of squeaks and a sense of fluttering.

"Clumsy oaf!" whispered Ro. "Now we must wait for them to quiet down again."

"A creepy place! One would expect it to be haunted."

"Some are. King Amentik's tomb has a deadly demon with wings, beak, and claws. Three men who invaded it were torn to bits."

Gezun tried for another bat and caught it. The bat bit his fingers, although its tiny teeth failed to draw blood.

In exploring one passage, they came to a place where a large block had fallen from the ceiling. Gezun trod on something hard and looked down. There were human bones on the floor, some half under the block.

"The kings put such gins in their tombs to foil robbers," said Ro. "When you step on a particular stone—boom! The ceiling falls on your head, or you fall through a trapdoor. I know many such traps, some not yet sprung."

"Hm. I see your father cares not what befalls me when I go to hunt bats by myself."

"Oh, no! We do not wish you slain while you are still useful to us!"

"How kind of you!"

"Fear not; I shall tell you where to hunt each day."

After several hours' hunting, the bat-bag was comfortably full of squeaking, fluttering captives. It moved with a life of its own.

"That will do for today," said Ro. "Let us go back to the entrance and eat."

"I hope you know your way through this maze. Why

did the kings put all these tunnels in their tombs? To mislead trespassers?"

"Partly, but also to serve as meeting-places for their cults and to store their treasure, their archives, and the mummies of their kin. You'll find little treasure now, though."

At the entrance they opened the food-bag. When Gezun had eaten and drunk, he looked more closely at Ro. She was a pretty little thing. Like most women of Typhon, she wore a tight short dress that covered her from knee to midriff. A strap rose from the front of the dress, between her bare breasts, and encircled her neck.

Gezun ran a hand up and down her body. She slapped the hand away. "My father warned you! Tety might be watching."

Gezun let it go. There would be more opportunities.

*

Back in Ugaph's quarters, Ro cut the throats of the bats and bled them into a bowl, while Ugaph burned incense and chanted an incantation. When Ro had finished, there was hardly more than a big spoonful of blood in the bowl. Something appeared in the magic circle Ugaph had drawn.

At first Gezun thought it was a cat, but it was a kind of small fox with a snub nose and enormous ears. It frisked around the circle and whined. Ugaph picked up the bowl, saying:

"What news, Tety?"

The familiar spoke in a shrill bark: "The ruby in the left eye of the statue of Ip, in the temple of Ip, is loose."

"Not very helpful, as the statue is higher than a man and set back from a railing. What else?"

"The front rung in the chair of the high-priest in the temple of Neb is also loose. I think not that you can get the rung out without tools, but the golden sheathing is cracked and easily torn off . . ."

After several such responses, Tety said: "I have told you all. Now my blood!"

Ugaph put the bowl inside the circle. The beast lapped up the blood and vanished.

"What's that?" asked Gezun.

"A fennec," said Ugaph. "Now that you are an initiate bat-hunter, I shall take Ro tomorrow. I will try that ruby in the temple of Ip. If she can make a disturbance—say by fainting—I'll knock the gem from its socket with that staff of yours and push it into a recess in the base of the statue. It is an ornate thing, full of hiding-places. Then, after a few days, I'll slip back in and take the ruby."

"Ho!" said Gezun. "You'll not send me hunting bats by myself yet. Think you I wish to be gobbled by some demon or fall through a trapdoor?"

"Ro can tell you what to do."

"I won't do it alone."

"You shall!"

"I will not."

"I'll set the mob on you!"

"Try it. They'd be interested in your little hoard of stolen sacred things."

"Well then, when will you be able to hunt by yourself?"

"It will take many days of Ro's guidance."

"He's right, father," said Ro. "If we ask too great risks from him, he'll flee."

"Oh, very well, very well. Though so far you've been of no use to me, and you eat enough for three."

*

Next day Ugaph, still grumbling, departed on his business while Gezun and Ro went back to the tombs. Again Gezun made exploratory passes and was rebuffed. When he pulled her into his arms she burst into tears, babbling of her father and his demons. Gezun let her go, not because he feared Ugaph and Tety, but because he was of too kindly nature to make the girl suffer.

So it went for a quarter-moon. Gezun made advances and accepted repulses until one day Ro began to weep almost before he started.

"What now?" he asked.

"Oh, Gezun, see you not? I am truly fond of you; it is all I can do to hold you off. When you look at me with those great brown eyes my sinews turn to water. Yet if you got me with child, my father would slay me."

"I'll take care of him."

"You talk folly. He could cut our throats any night while you lie snoring like a cataract."

"Then let's not go back to your catacombs, but flee to Kham."

"Father would charge you with felicide before the magistrate, and King Zeremab's chariots would overtake us on the road."

"Shall I cut your father's throat, then?"

"Nay, not that! I should be accursed forever."

"Oh, come, you don't believe that. Your father's a skeptic."

"I know not what to believe. He cares nought for me. All he wants is for me to keep my virginity until he has sold me to a rich husband. As though one of Typhon's lords would wed the daughter of a temple-thief! But I would not have him slain, especially as Tety might warn him and give him a chance to strike first."

*

Back in the hideaway they found Ugaph pale and trembly.

"It was a near thing today," he said. "A very near thing. I tried for that ruby in Ip's eye and came a hair's breadth from being caught."

"What happened?" said Gezun.

"I started to thrust with the staff at the eye when a priest came round the corner. He called me a blaspheming robber. He would have given me up to the soldiers had I not pacified him with a large offering and a tale of wishing to draw magical power from the statue. Now I must hide for a time. This priest will have warned his colleagues to watch for me."

"Let me get your supper," said Ro. "Then you'll feel better."

"It is all your fault for not having come with me. I am a poor old benefactor of humanity, but nobody gives me a chance. If there were gods, they would not let the universe run so unjustly."

All through supper, Ugaph whined about the way the world treated him. After supper, over a game of checkers with Gezun, he said:

"For once I think you foreigners are right about Setesh."

"How so?"

"They are a peevish, ungrateful lot, blindly groveling before the most cruel and gloomy gods their priests can imagine, while spurning enlighteners like me."

"Agile fellows!"

Ugaph, who seldom laughed and never saw the point of a joke, went on: "Curse of the green hippopotamus, that one of my virtue should be so put upon! This is no life for my daughter. How shall she catch a rich husband while lurking in these crypts?"

"Why not change your ways?"

"What can I do? There is no reward for the lifter of superstition. Whoever thinks up some new and bloodthirstier divinity makes his fortune, whilst I starve in squalor—"

"Why not make our fortunes the same way?"

Ugaph stopped in mid-move, holding a draftsman. "My boy, forgive my occasional harsh words. That was a proposal of genius."

"We'll make our god the ghastliest of all. He shall hate everybody and pursue his victims unto the third and fourth generation unless propitiated by huge offerings."

"Just so! He shall demand human sacrifices, to be slain with hideous tortures."

"Why human sacrifices?"

"The Typhonians love the spectacle."

"Well," said Gezun doubtfully, "I don't mind fleecing the Typhonians, but that's going too far."

"It is a common custom here."

"So? How do you go about it?"

"One gets a license."

"But whom do you sacrifice?"

"One buys slaves or kidnaps a foreigner off the street. Nobody minds if he be not of a nation with whom the king has a treaty."

"You mean I could have been seized by some gang all the time I've been here and hauled off to a temple for carving?"

"Surely, surely. Who cares for foreign devils?"

"Well, I care for this foreign devil and will not encourage a practice that might bring my own doom. Besides, it's not a Pusadian custom. If you want my help, there shall be no more talk of that."

Ugaph argued, sulked, and gave in. Thus it came to pass that, a quarter-moon later, a peasant on the outskirts of Typhon, hoeing his plot, struck a bronzen tablet.

"Praise be to Neb!" he cried as he dug it up and brushed the dirt off. The tablet was inscribed, though he could not read. It weighed about a pound.

Two men who had been sauntering down the nearby road came over: a snaggle-toothed middle-aged Seteshan and a gigantic young foreigner.

"What is that?" said the middle-aged one.

"I have done nought wrong, my lord," said the peasant. "I found this just now. It was on this plot, which I own in freehold, and so belongs to me."

"What will you do with it?"

"Sell it to a dealer in metals, my lord."

"Hm. Let's have a look at it."

The peasant put the tablet behind him. He could not hide it in his clothes because he wore none. "No you don't, sir. You will snatch it and run, and then where shall I be?"

"All right, you hold it and let me look at it."

Some peasants in the neighboring fields came over to see what was going on. Some travelers on the road stopped too, so presently there were a score of people around Ugaph, Gezun, and the farmer. Ugaph tilted the plaque and read loudly:

"I, Ka the Appalling, eldest and father of the gods, creator and master of the seven universes, shall soon come to dwell in Typhon in the land of Setesh. Woe to the sinners of Typhon! Now you shall be under my very eye. For, I am a great, fierce, and jealous god, at whose very name the other gods tremble. Where they beat you with switches, I shall beat you with cudgels; where they smote the sinner, I shall smite all his kin, neighbors, and friends. Repent ere it be too late! I, Ka the Omnipotent, have spoken."

Ugaph said: "This is surely a portentous matter. Fellow, I will give you half the weight of this tablet in silver, which is more trade-metal than you would normally see in a lifetime. Then I shall take it into the city to see what the wise priests of Typhon make of it."

"Aye, take it!" said the peasant.

*

A few days later, when the rumor of the finding of the tablet had gone around, Ugaph appeared in the agora. He was naked, with red stripes on his face and ashes on his body. He foamed at the mouth (by chewing soapwort) and altogether was the holiest-looking thing the Typhonians had seen in a long time. He waved the tablet, cried its message in a loud voice, and called upon the people to repent. Gezun went about with a basket to catch the wedges and rings and bars of trade-metal they tossed into it.

"A temple for Ka the Appalling!" shrieked Ugaph. "What will he think if he comes to Typhon and finds no god-house? What will he do? What will he do to us? It is our last chance . . ."

Gezun checked a smile. He composed Ugaph's speeches, since Ugaph's talents did not run that way. On the other hand, provided somebody put words in his mouth, the temple-thief made a fine prophet, being of naturally solemn and pompous mien.

After another half-moon, they were counting their wealth in the hideout. Ro sorted out the different metals while Ugaph and Gezun weighed them. Ugaph, who had some small education, added up the totals on the wall of the chamber with a burnt stick. He said:

"We have more here than I have made in my whole career as a collector. Why thought I not of this before?"

"Because I wasn't here to suggest it," grinned Gezun. "Now, know you what I'd suggest further?"

"What?"

"That we put this stuff in stout bags and get out of Typhon. We could go to Kham. Your share will keep you in comfort the rest of your life, and mine will take me to all the places I have not yet seen."

"Are you mad, stripling?"

"What mean you?"

"This is nothing to what we shall collect once we get our temple built."

"You mean you would go through with that scheme and not merely talk about it?"

"Surely, surely. I have already seen Sentiu the building-contractor and visited the artist Heqatari. He shall design our temple and the statue of the god."

"Then give me my half, and stay here with yours."

"No! We shall need it all. And think not to take your share by stealth. Remember, it was not I who slew the sacred cat."

Gezun glared but subsided. Ugaph might be right at that; he had had more experience at this sort of thing.

*

Soon the site of the temple sounded with hammering. Walls rose, floors were laid, and in the midst of it all the great Heqatari worked with his apprentices on the statue. It was to be an imposing affair of gilded bronze, showing a vulture-headed Ka with multiple wings and arms, hurling thunderbolts and brandishing weapons.

When the workmen stopped for their noon meal, Gezun went around to where Heqatari and his apprentices gnawed bread and cheese in the shade of a wall.

"Greetings, great artist," said Gezun. "Can you explain something?"

"What?"

"What's that walled section in the rear, with the deep embayment? It was not in the original plan," Gezun pointed.

"You must mean the stable."

"Stable?"

"Aye. Ugaph has bought a chariot and pair and wishes room to store them on the temple grounds."

"Why, the foul—" began Gezun, where the clopping of hooves made him turn. There came Ugaph, standing in a gold-trimmed chariot drawn by a pair of whites. He reined up, cursing as the horses skittered and bucked and the workmen grinned at his lack of skill. Gezun strode over and began:

"What's this folly? And what mean you by commanding an enlargement of the temple without my knowledge?"

Ugaph's face darkened. "Keep your voice down, stripling, or I shall raise mine too. I might even speak of cats."

Gezun almost sprang upon Ugaph, but mastered his rage and said: "We shall speak of this again." He walked off.

They had a furious quarrel in the underground chambers that night, Gezun pounding the table and shouting: "You profligate old fool! We're in debt far enough now to put us into debt-slavery for our lives."

"And who told you how to run a cult? You think a babe like you, a third my age and a barbarian to boot, can teach me the art?"

"I can tell when an enterprise is being run to death. Instead of getting out with your paint and ashes and digging more gold out of the Typhonians, you swank around in embroidered robes and drive your gaudy toy."

"That shows your ignorance. By showing the mob how successful we are, we prove our god is truly mighty."

"Said the drunken yokel who fell down the well, how clever I am, for now I shall never be thirsty! I want my share of our property, now!"

"You cannot have it. It is tied up in the temple."

"Sell my interest in it, or borrow it. But I want that trade-metal."

"Impossible, you dog. When we have made our fortunes, you may ask."

"I'll go to law to force a division."

"See how far you get when the magistrate hears you are a felicide!"

Gezun started to rise, murder in his eyes, when Ro seized his arm, crying: "Gezun! Calm yourself! He has powers!"

A squeak from the corner made them turn. There sat Tety the demon in fennec-form.

"O master!" whined the fox. "It is long since you have fed me. Can I do nought for you?"

"No," said Ugaph. "Begone and bother me not."

"Pray, master! I must have bats' blood. I perish for want of the mystic ingredients."

"Begone!" yelled Ugaph, and ripped out an exorcism. The familiar vanished.

Gezun's temper had cooled, so the quarrel was dropped. For several days Ugaph worked at his evangelism, crying doom about the agora while Gezun collected. Gezun noted that the collections were dwindling.

"By Neb's toenails, it will soon not be worth while," grumbled Ugaph one evening. "All the Typhonians have heard our message and await something new. We must hurry the temple."

"How long will it take?" said Gezun. "By Sentiu's original promises it should be done, but the roof is not yet up."

"That is the way with builders. I see where we made several mistakes, but when we build our big temple those shall be corrected."

"What big temple?"

"Oh, this is only a small affair. As our cult grows, this building will not hold our congregation. We shall build a magnificent structure like the temple of Sekhemet."

"Hump. You mean after you've paid off my share."

"Why so eager to withdraw?"

"I tire of Typhon. They hate foreigners as one would expect of some backward Atlantean village, but not of a great city. Besides, it is too hot, and the fleas and flies give one no peace."

Ugaph shrugged. "Each to his taste. Tomorrow I will oversee the putting up of the roof."

Next morning, after Ugaph left, Gezun was loafing and watching Ro clean up their breakfast. Tety appeared, whining: "Good foreign devil, my master neglects and spurns me. I starve for bats' blood."

"That's sad, little one," said Gezun.

"Can you do nought for me?"

Gezun started to say no, then grinned and said to Ro: "Beautiful, those bat-hunts were fun. Let's make another."

"But that long walk? In this heat?"

"We'll use the chariot. It's half mine. And the tombs are cool."

"Oh, bless you, dear mortal!" said Tety.

Hours later they were deep in the bowels of King Khephru's pyramid. When their game-bag was full they went to the entrance and ate. Then Gezun pulled Ro to him and kissed him. She resisted, but not enough, so that what started as a youthful game turned into a real love-tussle. A little later Gezun slept in the tunnel-entrance, snoring thunderously, while Ro wept for her lost maidenhood and covered his face with damp kisses.

*

Ugaph hung around the temple until Heqatari flew into a tantrum. He cursed Ugaph and all his ancestors because, he said, Ugaph got in his way, distracted him by idiotic suggestions, and did not understand that the artistic soul was purer and finer than the souls of common men.

Ugaph, disgruntled, went to the stable where he kept his chariot. He was even more vexed to learn that his partner had taken the vehicle. Scowling, he walked to the palace and gained admittance to the office of the Registrar of Licenses. He asked for a license for human sacrifice.

"You know the rules?" said the Registrar.

"Surely, surely, my lord. Pusadians are not among the protected groups of foreigners, are they?"

"What are Pusadians?"

"Far-western barbarians. Is everything in order, then?"

"The priests of Neb and Shekhemet and the others are up in arms over your competition, but we cannot afford to offend any god. So here is your license."

"I abase myself in humble gratitude, my lord. Come to one of our services."

Ugaph backed out, bowing. Next he went to the thieves' quarter, a tumbledown part of the city where people were either too poor to escape or sought refuge there from King Zeremab's soldiers and officials. He sought out a brawny cutthroat named Eha, whom he had known in his thieving days. He said:

"Are you looking for work, old comrade?"

Eha grinned and flexed a muscle. "I might, if it meant enough metal and not too much work."

"I need a couple of stout fellows to help me with the temple: to sweep the floor, guard the loot, the like. Have you a friend I could trust?"

"What about that foreign devil, your partner?"

"I think we shall not long be troubled with him. Are you up to desperate deeds?"

"You know me, Ugaph."

Eha got his friend, a silent hulk named Maatab. Ugaph took them to the temple and put them to work on small tasks, such as moving the gear from the hideaway to the temple when the dwelling-rooms were finished.

Gezun made only a mild objection to hiring this pair, as Ugaph explained that three could not do all the work of the cult. Gezun was going about starry-eyed, as he had decided he was in love again. Ugaph, who might have been expected to notice the signs that Gezun and Ro gave of their attachment, seemed to pay no attention.

*

The day came when the last bit of plaster had dried, the last mural had been painted, and the last patch of gold-leaf had been hammered into place. Ugaph called Gezun, Ro, Maatab, and Eha into conference. He sat at the head of the table in a gold-embroidered robe of shiny eastern stuff and a tall pointed hat. He said:

"Tomorrow night is our dedication. The temple will be filled. I have bought an ox for sacrifice to get things started. However, our future depends on this ceremony's going smoothly, to get our pious fools worked up to a big donation. Let us be sure we all know our parts perfectly . . ."

When they had rehearsed again, Ugaph said: "Gezun! Maatab and Eha and I go to fetch our ox. I leave you here to guard the temple. We shall be gone an hour."

He led two thieves out. Gezun looked at Ro. He had not been alone with her for any length of time since that day in Khephru's tomb. All that made him hesitate was that Ugaph's parting words sounded almost like an invitation. But, for one of Gezun's age and vigor, the contest between lust and suspicion was too one-sided to last long.

Ugaph led Maatab and Eha to the main chamber of the temple. In front of the statue of Ka, Ugaph said: "How is your courage?"

Maatab laughed, and Eha made muscles.

"Good," murmured Ugaph. "The plan I have discussed is the one that young dog thinks we shall follow. What we shall really do is this. He will be in his room at the beginning of the service, primping. He will come out thinking he is to enter the main chamber and slay the ox with the sanctified ax. But you two—"

Eha broke in: "Is it wise to talk of this so near the god?" He jerked his head towards the brooding idol.

"Ha! That is but a thing of bronze and wood. I planned it and Heqatari made it, just as I invented Ka and his whole cult. Unless we believe in a god he cannot exist." Ugaph spat at the statue. "If you fear . . ."

"I? Fear?" protested both thieves at once.

"Well then, listen. As Gezun steps from his room, you two shall seize him. Slay him not, nor even stun him deeply. I wish him awake during the sacrifice; the throng loves the screams of the victim. Bind his wrists and ankles firmly and bear him to the main chamber. Lay him on the altar, and I shall do the rest . . ."

*

In his chamber, Gezun could hear the voices of the congregation as Ugaph led them in a hymn, for which Ro played a lyre. He put the last touches on his costume: a knee-length kilt embroidered with gold thread gilded sandals, and an ornate conical cap like Ugaph's but not so tall. His listened for his cue. When it came, he stepped to the leathern curtain in the doorway. His hand was out to thrust the curtain aside when he heard a squeak. There was Tety.

"Gezun!" said the familiar.

"What is it?"

"There is something you must know—"

"No time! Tell me after the service." Gezun reached for the curtain again.

"It is a matter of life and death."

"By the holy crocodile of Haides! Eha and Maatab will be leading in the ox. Save it till later."

"But it is your death! They will slay you instead of the ox."

Gezun stopped. "What's this?"

Tety told of Ugaph's orders. "I was hovering in my spirit form in the temple and came to warn you because of that bats' blood."

"But why should Ugaph slay me?"

"To get sole ownership, to give the Typhonians a gory show, and to see that you shall not object to such sacrifices in the future."

Gezun saw he had been a fool. With a smothered curse he leaped for his belongings and got out the double-curved Tartessian sword. "We shall see who sacrifices whom!"

"Go not unto the main chamber!"

"Why not?"

"I know not, but there are portentous stirrings on the spiritual plane. Something dreadful will happen."

"Hm. Anyway, my thanks, little devil."

Gezun went to the doorway on tiptoe. He stood to one side of the door and jerked the curtain aside. Seeing movement in the dark corridor, he snatched. He caught a muscular arm. With a mighty heave he pulled Eha into the room.

Eha struck at Gezun with a short leaden bludgeon. As Eha was off-balance at the time, the blow did not hit squarely. It knocked off Gezun's wizard's hat and grazed his shaven scalp, filling his eyes with stars. He thrust the sword into Eha's neck.

Eha stumbled to hands and knees with a gurgle, dropping the club. Maatab bounded into the room. Gezun tried to withdraw the sword from Eha, but it stuck fast. Then Maatab was upon him.

They staggered back into the middle of the room, kicking, punching, gouging, and grabbing for holds. Maatab hooked a thumb into Gezun's nostrils, but Gezun kicked Maatab in the crotch and sent the Seteshan back groaning. They clinched, fell, and rolled. Gezun felt the bludgeon under his hand. He picked it up and struck at Maatab. The blow struck Maatab's shoulder. Maatab broke away and tore the sword out of Eha.

Then they were up again, feinting, dodging, and striking. Each leaped at the other for a finishing blow, but each caught the other's wrist. They staggered about, each trying to wrench his right arm out of the other's grasp. Gezun felt a grip on his ankle. It was Eha, not yet dead. Gezun fell heavily. Maatab leaped for him, but Gezun flung up both legs and drove his heels into Maatab's belly. The Seteshan was flung back against the wall. He dropped the sword and half fell, coughing and gasping.

Gezun rose and lunged for the sword. There was an instant of floundering as each tried to pick up the weapon and at the same time to kick aside or stamp on the other's groping hand. Then Gezun kicked the sword out into the middle of the room. He scooped it up and straightened to slash at Maatab, who turned and half fell out the doorway.

*

To kill time, Ugaph had stretched his sermon, reiterating the awfulness, ferocity, and vindictiveness of Ka the Appalling. Then, instead of a bound Gezun being carried out by Eha and Maatab, Maatab appeared running with Gezun after him.

Maatab stumbled around to the front of the statue, trying to cry a warning but too winded to speak. Both were disheveled, their kilts torn, their faces and bodies covered by bruises and scratches. Sweat and blood ran down their limbs. Ro dropped her lyre with a twang.

"He—he—" gasped Maatab, dodging behind Ugaph.

"I'll—" panted Gezun.

Ugaph retreated towards the crowd, shrieking: "Seize the felicide! He is the foreign devil who slew the cat in the Month of the Camel! Tear him to pieces!"

A murmur in the congregation rose to a roar. Much as Gezun wanted to see the blood of Ugaph and Maatab spurt, he did not wish to be torn to bits afterwards. The crowd fell silent. He stepped back towards the statue and glanced at Ro.

Ro was staring at a point behind him and some feet over his head. He looked up. An arm of gilded bronze, ending in a clawed hand like the foot of a bird of prey, was coming down upon him.

Gezun made a tremendous leap. The wind of the snatch fanned his back.

With a loud creaking, the statue stepped heavily down from its dais. Ugaph and Maatab stared in unbelieving horror, while behind them the audience began to scream and stampede.

Ugaph and Maatab turned to run, but two long arms

shot out. One arm seized each man, the claws sinking deeply. Ka raised the two kicking, screaming men towards his vulture's beak.

Gezun caught Ro's wrist and dragged her through the other door. Back in the corridor he started for the door to the stable. Then he said:

"Wait! Hold this!"

"But Gezun—"

He pressed his sword into her hands and darted into Ugaph's chamber. On the floor lay the chest containing their liquid funds. It was locked and chained to a ring in the wall. Gezun picked up the chest and gave it a mighty heave as if to throw it. On the first try the chain held, but on the second the staple pulled out of the wall. Gezun ran out with the chest under one arm.

The screams from the main chamber of the temple came higher and higher. They faded behind Gezun as he pulled Ro out to the stable, hitched up the whites, whirled the chariot around, and set out for the north gate at a gallop. They skidded around turns.

"What—what happened?" said Ro.

"You father didn't believe in Ka, but he convinced so many others that their belief called the god to life."

"But why did Ka animate the statue and attack Father?"

"Well, he was described as fierce and vindictive, so he'd be angry when I wasn't sacrificed as promised. Or perhaps he resented Ugaph's atheism." He slowed the team to a trot. "Let's stop at the fountain to make ourselves look respectable, for the guards won't let us out the gate."

A few minutes later, Gezun whipped up the whites and galloped out on the long level desert road to Kham in the land of Kheru. Behind him, a somber shadow seemed to brood over Typhon.

"Anyway," he said. "I'm through with experiments having to do with gods. Men are hard enough to deal with."

Jack Vance

Turjan of Miir

I SUSPECT many science fiction writers would really
rather be fantasy writers, if they had their druthers. If
you were to ask me which living sf writer most resembles
the great fantasy masters of old, I would unhesitatingly
name Jack Vance first. He writes with a great sense of
style, with polish, sparkle and wit. The surface of his
prose glitters with exotic, fascinating names. It blazes
with pyrotechnic ideas and original concepts, which he
seems to toss off almost effortlessly. He is at once one of
the most entertaining, and talented and thoroughly original of all science fiction writers. And (thank the Valar!)
one of the most prolific.

Jack Vance was born in San Francisco; raised on a
ranch in central California; when I last heard from him,
he was living in Oakland. He studied mining engineering, then physics, then English, then journalism—and
came away from each of these knowing he did not, after
all, want to be an engineer, a physicist, an English
teacher or a journalist. In the late 1940's he turned to
writing science fiction, and decided that he had found
his field at last. Now about 50, he has been writing ever
since, and he has published around thirty or so books.
Among them are *The Dragon Masters*, which won a
Hugo at the 1963 World Science Fiction Convention,
and *The Last Castle*, which won a 1967 Nebula award

given by the Science Fiction Writers of America as well as one of the 1967 Hugoes.

As far as the imaginary world fantasy is concerned, Jack Vance has written very little. But that little is of such extraordinary brilliance that, to my taste, at least, it outweighs all of his admittedly excellent science fiction.

In 1950, Vance published a book called *The Dying Earth*. It was an oddly constructed little book, a series of interlocking short stories which sort of opened into each other like one of those Chinese puzzle-boxes our grandmothers used to own. The tales were set here on earth, but at an enormous distance in the future. New races of man had evolved, new species of beast; science had vanished and magic had arisen to dominate the twilight of our world as it dominated earth's morning.

The Dying Earth was published by an obscure paperback house called Hillman. Distribution was awful (I don't think *The Dying Earth* was distributed at all on the east coast—I received my copy as a gift from some fans in Portland, Oregon). But a good book has lasting qualities: *The Dying Earth* was not allowed to die. Years after that first printing, it was reissued by another publishing house and has been kept in print ever since.

The tale I have selected is a perfect example of Vance at the top of his form, tossing off sparkling ideas with a liberal hand, working in a mood of strangeness and melancholy that is evocative, jewelling the surface of his prose with gorgeous invented names . . . .

———◆———

TURJAN SAT in his workroom, legs sprawled out from the stool, back against and elbows on the bench. Across the room was a cage; into this Turjan gazed with rueful vexation. The creature in the cage returned the scrutiny with emotions beyond conjecture.

It was a thing to arouse pity—a great head on a small spindly body, with weak rheumy eyes and a flabby button of a nose. The mouth hung slackly wet, the skin glistened waxy pink. In spite of its manifest imperfection, it was to date the most successful product of Turjan's vats.

Turjan stood up, found a bowl of pap. With a long-handled spoon he held food to the creature's mouth. But the mouth refused the spoon and mush trickled down the glazed skin to fall on the rickety frame.

Turjan put down the bowl, stood back and slowly returned to his stool. For a week now it had refused to eat. Did the idiotic visage conceal perception, a will to extinction? As Turjan watched, the white-blue eyes closed, the great head slumped and bumped to the floor of the cage. These limbs relaxed: the creature was dead.

Turjan sighed and left the room. He mounted winding stone stairs and at last came out on the roof of his castle Miir, high above the river Derna. In the west the sun hung close to old earth; ruby shafts, heavy and rich as wine, slanted past the gnarled boles of the archaic forest to lay on the turfed forest floor. The sun sank in accordance with the old ritual; latter-day night fell across the forest, a soft, warm darkness came swiftly, and Turjan stood pondering the death of his latest creature.

He considered its many precursors: the thing all eyes, the boneless creature with the pulsing surface of its brain exposed, the beautiful female body whose intestines trailed out into the nutrient solution like seeking fibrils, the inverted inside-out creatures . . . Turjan sighed bleakly. His methods were at fault; a fundamental element was lacking from his synthesis, a matrix ordering the components of the pattern.

As he sat gazing across the darkening land, memory took Turjan to a night of years before, when the Sage had stood beside him.

"In ages gone," the Sage had said, his eyes fixed on a low star, "a thousand spells were known to sorcery and the wizard's effected their wills. Today, as Earth dies, a hundred spells remain to man's knowledge, and these have come to us through the ancient books . . . But there is one called Pandelume, who knows all the spells, all the incantations, cantraps, runes, and thaumaturgies that have ever wrenched and molded space . . ." He had fallen silent, lost in his thoughts.

"Where is this Pandelume?" Turjan had asked presently.

"He dwells in the land of Embelyon," the Sage had replied, "but where this land lies, no one knows."

"How does one find Pandelume, then?"

The Sage had smiled faintly. "If it were ever necessary, a spell exists to take one there."

Both had been silent a moment; then the Sage had spoken, staring out over the forest.

"One may ask anything of Pandelume, and Pandelume will answer—provided that the seeker performs the service Pandelume requires. And Pandelume drives a hard bargain."

Then the Sage had shown Turjan the spell in question, which he had discovered in an ancient portfolio, and kept secret from all the world.

Turjan, remembering this conversation, descended to his study, a long low hall with stone walls and a stone floor deadened by a thick russet rug. The tomes which held Turjan's sorcery lay on the long table of black skeel or were thrust helter-skelter into shelves. These were volumes compiled by many wizards of the past, untidy folios collected by the Sage, leather-bound librams setting forth the syllables of a hundred powerful spells, so cogent that Turjan's brain could know but four at a time.

Turjan found a musty portfolio, turned the heavy pages to the spell the Sage had shown him, the Call to the Violent Cloud. He stared down at the characters and they burned with an urgent power, pressing off the page as if frantic to leave the dark solitude of the book.

Turjan closed the book, forcing the spell back into oblivion. He robed himself with a short blue cape; tucked a blade into his belt, fitted the amulet holding Laccodel's Rune to his wrist. Then he sat down and from a journal chose the spells he would take with him. What dangers he might meet he could not know, so he selected three spells of general application: the Excellent

Prismatic Spray, Phandaal's Mantle of Stealth, and the Spell of the Slow Hour.

He climbed the parapets of his castle and stood under the far stars, breathing the air of ancient Earth . . . How many times had this air been breathed before him? What cries of pain had this air experienced, what sighs, laughs, war shouts, cries of exultation, gasps . . .

The night was wearing on. A blue light wavered in the forest. Turjan watched a moment, then at last squared himself and uttered the Call to the Violent Cloud.

All was quiet; then came a whisper of movement swelling to a roar of great winds. A wisp of white appeared and waxed to a pillar of boiling black smoke. A voice deep and harsh issued from the turbulence.

"At your disturbing power is this instrument come; whence will you go?"

"Four Directions, then One," said Turjan. "Alive must I be brought to Embelyon."

The cloud whirled down; far up and away he was snatched, flung head over heels into incalculable distance. Four directions was he thrust, then one, and at last a great blow hurled him from the cloud, sprawled him into Embelyon.

Turjan gained his feet and tottered a moment, half-dazed. His senses steadied; he looked about him.

He stood on the bank of a limpid pool. Blue flowers grew about his ankles and at his back reared a grove of tall blue-green trees, the leaves blurring on high into mist. Was Embelyon of Earth? The trees were Earth-like, the flowers were of familiar form, the air was of the same texture . . . But there was an odd lack to this land and it was difficult to determine. Perhaps it came of the horizon's curious vagueness, perhaps from the blurring quality of the air, lucent and uncertain as water. Most strange, however, was the sky, a mesh of vast ripples and cross-ripples, and these refracted a thousand shafts of colored light, rays which in mid-air wove wondrous laces, rainbow nets, in all the jewel hues. So as Turjan watched, there swept over him beams of claret, topaz, rich violet, radiant green. He now perceived that the colors of the flowers and the trees were but fleeting functions of the sky, for now the flowers were of salmon tint, and the trees a dreaming purple. The flowers deepened to copper, then with a suffusion of crimson, warmed through maroon to scarlet, and the trees had become sea-blue.

"The Land None Knows Where," said Turjan to himself. "Have I been brought high, low, into a pre-existence or into the after-world?" He looked toward the horizon and thought to see a black curtain raising high into the murk, and this curtain encircled the hand in all directions.

The sound of galloping hooves approached; he turned to find a black horse lunging break-neck along the bank of the pool. The rider was a young woman with black hair streaming wildly. She wore loose white breeches to the knee and a yellow cape flapping in the wind. One hand clutched the reins, the other flourished a sword.

Turjan warily stepped aside, for her mouth was tight and white as if in anger, and her eyes glowed with a peculiar frenzy. The woman hauled back on the reins, wheeled her horse high around, charged Turjan, and struck out at him with her sword.

Turjan jumped back and whipped free his own blade. When she lunged at him again, he fended off the blow and leaning forward, touched the point to her arm and brought a drop of blood. She drew back startled; then up from her saddle she snatched a bow and flicked an arrow to the string. Turjan sprang forward, dodging the wild sweep of her sword, seized her around the waist, and dragged her to the ground.

She fought with a crazy violence. He had no wish to kill her, and so struggled in a manner not entirely dignified. Finally he held her helpless, her arms pinioned behind her back.

"Quiet, vixen!" said Turjan, "lest I lose patience and stun you!"

"Do as you please," the girl gasped. "Life and death are brothers."

"Why do you seek to harm me?" demanded Turjan. "I have given you no offense."

"You are evil, like all existence." Emotion ground the delicate fibers of her throat. "If power were mine, I would crush the universe to bloody gravel, and stamp it into the ultimate muck."

Turjan in surprise relaxed his grip, and she nearly broke loose. But he caught her again.

"Tell me, where may I find Pandelume?"

The girl stilled her exertion, twisted her head to stare at Turjan. Then: "Search all Embelyon. I will assist you not at all."

If she were more amiable, thought Turjan, she would be a creature of remarkable beauty.

"Tell me where I may find Pandelume," said Turjan, "else I find other uses for you."

She was silent for a moment, her eyes blazing with madness. Then she spoke in a vibrant voice.

"Pandelume dwells beside the stream only a few paces distant."

Turjan released her, but he took her sword and bow. "If I return these to you, will you go your way in peace?"

For a moment she glared; then without words she mounted her horse and rode off through the trees.

Turjan watched her disappear through the shafts of jewel colors, then went in the direction she had indicated. Soon he came to a long low manse of red stone backed by dark trees. As he approached the door swung open. Turjan halted in mid-stride.

"Enter!" came a voice. "Enter, Turjan of Miir!"

So Turjan wonderingly entered the manse of Pandelume. He found himself in a tapestried chamber, bare of furnishing save a single settee. No one came to greet him. A closed door stood at the opposite wall, and Turjan went to pass through, thinking perhaps it was expected of him.

"Halt, Turjan," spoke the voice. "No one may gaze on Pandelume. It is the law."

Turjan, standing in the middle of the room, spoke to his unseen host.

"This is my mission, Pandelume," he said. "For some time I have been striving to create humanity in my vats. Yet always I fail, from ignorance of the agent that binds and orders the patterns. This master-matrix must be known to you; therefore I come to you for guidance."

"Willingly will I aid you," said Pandelume. "There is, however, another aspect involved. The universe is methodized by symmetry and balance; in every aspect of existence is this equipoise observed. Consequently, even in the trivial scope of our dealings, this equivalence must be maintained, thus and thus. I agree to assist you; in return, you perform a service of equal value for me. When you have completed this small work, I will instruct and guide you to your complete satisfaction."

"What may this service be?" inquired Turjan.

"A man lives in the land of Ascolais, not far from your Castle Miir. About his neck hangs an amulet of carved blue stone. This you must take from him and bring to me."

Turjan considered a moment.

"Very well," he said. "I will do what I can. Who is the man?"

Pandelume answered in a soft voice.

"Prince Kandive the Golden."

"Ah," exclaimed Turjan ruefully, "you have gone to no pains to make my task a pleasant one . . . But I will fulfill your requirement as best I can."

"Good," said Pandelume. "Now I must instruct you. Kandive wears this amulet hidden below his singlet. When an enemy appears, he takes it out to display on his chest, such is the potency of the charm. No matter what else, do not gaze on this amulet, either before or after you take it, on pain of most hideous consequence."

"I understand," said Turjan. "I will obey. Now there is a question I would ask—providing the answer will not involve me in an undertaking to bring the Moon back to Earth, or recover an elixir you inadvertently spilled in the sea."

Pandelume laughed loud. "Ask on," he responded, "and I will answer."

Turjan put his question.

"As I approached your dwelling, a woman of insane fury wished to kill me. This I would not permit and she departed in rage. Who is this woman and why is she thus?"

Pandelume's voice was amused. "I, too," he replied, "have vats where I mold life into varied forms. This girl T'sais I created, but I wrought carelessly, with a flaw in the synthesis. So she climbed from the vat with a warp in her brain, in this manner: what we hold to be beautiful seems to her loathsome and ugly, and what we find ugly is to her intolerably vile, in a degree that you and I cannot understand. She finds the world a bitter place, people with shapes of direst malevolence."

"So this is the answer," Turjan murmured. "Pitiable wretch!"

"Now," said Pandelume, "you must be on your way to Kaiin; the auspices are good . . . In a moment open this door, enter, and move to the pattern of runes on the floor."

Turjan performed as he was bid. He found the next room to be circular and high-domed, with the varying lights of Embelyon pouring down through sky-transparencies. When he stood upon the pattern in the floor, Pandelume spoke again.

"Now close your eyes, for I must enter and touch you. Heed well, do not try to glimpse me!"

Turjan closed his eyes. Presently a step sounded behind him. "Extend your hand," said the voice. Turjan did so, and felt a hard object placed therein. "When your mission is accomplished, crush this crystal and at once you will find yourself in this room." A cold hand was laid on his shoulder.

"An instant you will sleep," said Pandelume. "When you awake you will be in the city Kaiin."

The hand departed. A dimness came over Turjan as he stood awaiting the passage. The air had suddenly become full of sound: clattering, a tinkling of many small

bells, music, voices. Turjan frowned, pursed his lips: A
strange tumult for the austere home of Pandelume!

A woman's voice sounded close by.

"Look, O Santanil, see the man-owl who closes his
eyes to merriment!"

There was a man's laughter, suddenly hushed. "Come.
The fellow is bereft and possibly violent. Come."

Turjan hesitated, then opened his eyes. It was night in
white-walled Kaiin, and festival time. Orange lanterns
floated in the air, moving as the breeze took them. From
the balconies dangled flower chains and cages of blue
flies. The streets surged with the wine-flushed popu-
lace, costumed in a multitude of bizarre modes. Here
was a Melantine bargeman, here a warrior of Valdaran's
Green Legion, here another of ancient times wearing
one of the old helmets. In a little cleared space a garlanded courtesan of the Kauchique littoral danced the
Dance of the Fourteen Silken Movements to the music
of flutes. In the shadow of a balcony a girl barbarian of
East Almery embraced a man blackened and in leather
harness as a Deodand of the forest. They were gay,
these people of waning Earth, feverishly merry, for infinite night was close at hand, when the red sun should
finally flicker and go black.

Turjan melted into the throng. At a tavern he re-
freshed himself with biscuits and wine; then he made
for the palace of Kandive the Golden.

The palace loomed before him, every window and
balcony aglow with light. Among the lords of the city
there was feasting and revelry. If Prince Kandive were
flushed with drink and unwary, reflected Turjan, the
task should not be too difficult. Yet, entering boldly, he
might be recognized, for he was known to many in
Kaiin. So, uttering Phandaal's Mantle of Stealth, he
faded from the sight of all men.

Through the arcade he slipped, into the grand salon,
where the lords of Kaiin made merry like the throngs of
the street. Turjan threaded the rainbow of silk, velour,
sateen, watching the play with amusement. On a terrace
some stood looking into a sunken pool where a pair of

captured Deodands, their skins like oiled jet, paddled and glared; others tossed darts at the spread-eagled body of a young Cobalt Mountain witch. In alcoves beflowered girls offered synthetic love to wheezing old men, and elsewhere others lay stupefied by dream-powders. Nowhere did Turjan find Prince Kandive. Through the palace he wandered, room after room, until at last in an upper chamber he came upon the tall golden-bearded prince, lolling on a couch with a masked girl-child who had green eyes and hair died pale green.

Some intuition or perhaps a charm warned Kandive when Turjan slipped through the purple hangings. Kandive leapt to his feet.

"Go!" he ordered the girl. "Out of the room quickly! Mischief moves somewhere near and I must blast it with magic!"

The girl ran hastily from the chamber. Kandive's hand stole to his throat and pulled forth the hidden amulet. But Turjan shielded his gaze with his hand.

Kandive uttered a powerful charm which loosened space free of all warp. So Turjan's spell was void and he became visible.

"Turjan of Miir skulks through my palace!" snarled Kandive.

"With ready death on my lips," spoke Turjan. "Turn your back, Kandive, or I speak a spell and run you through with my sword."

Kandive made as if to obey, but instead shouted the syllables bringing the Omnipotent Sphere about him.

"Now I call my guards, Turjan," announced Kandive contemptuously, "and you shall be cast to the Deodands in the tank."

Kandive did not know the engraved band Turjan wore on his wrist, a most powerful rune, maintaining a field solvent of all magic. Still guarding his vision against the amulet, Turjan stepped through the Sphere. Kandive's great blue eyes bulged.

"Call the guards," said Turjan. "They will find our body riddled by lines of fire."

"*Your* body, Turjan!" cried the Prince, babbling the

spell. Instantly the blazing wires of the Excellent Prismatic Spray lashed from all directions at Turjan. Kandive watched the furious rain with a wolfish grin, but his expression changed quickly to consternation. A finger's breadth from Turjan's skin the fire-darts dissolved into a thousand gray puffs of smoke.

"Turn your back, Kandive," Turjan ordered. "Your magic is useless against Laccodel's Rune." But Kandive took a step toward a spring in the wall.

"Halt!" cried Turjan. "One more step and the Spray splits you thousandfold!"

Kandive stopped short. In helpless rage he turned his back and Turjan, stepping forward quickly, reached over Kandive's neck, seized the amulet and raised it free. It crawled in his hand and through the fingers there passed a glimpse of blue. A daze shook his brain, and for an instant he heard a murmur of avid voices . . . His vision cleared. He backed away from Kandive, stuffing the amulet in his pouch. Kandive asked, "May I now turn about in safety?"

"When you wish," responded Turjan, clasping his pouch. Kandive, seeing Turjan occupied, negligently stepped to the wall and placed his hand on a spring.

"Turjan," he said, "you are lost. Before you may utter a syllable, I will open the floor and drop you a great dark distance. Can your charms avail against this?"

Turjan halted in mid-motion, fixed his eyes upon Kandive's red and gold face. Then he dropped his eyes sheepishly. "Ah, Kandive," he fretted, "you have outwitted me. If I return you the amulet, may I go free?"

"Toss the amulet at my feet," said Kandive, gloating. "Also Laccodel's Rune. Then I shall decide what mercy to grant you."

"Even the Rune?" Turjan asked, forcing a piteous note to his voice.

"Or your life."

Turjan reached into his pouch and grasped the crystal Pandelume had given him. He pulled it forth and held it against the pommel of his sword.

"Ho, Kandive," he said, "I have discerned your trick.

You merely wish to frighten me into surrender. I defy you!"

Kandive shrugged. "Die then." He pushed the spring. The floor jerked open, and Turjan disappeared into the gulf. But when Kandive raced below to claim Turjan's body, he found no trace, and he spent the rest of the night in temper, brooding over wine.

*

Turjan found himself in the circular room of Pandelume's manse. Embelyon's many-colored lights streamed through the sky-windows upon his shoulder—sapphire blue, the yellow of marigolds, blood red. There was a silence through the house. Turjan moved away from the rune in the floor glancing uneasily to the door, fearful lest Pandelume, unaware of his presence, enter the room.

"Pandelume!" he called. "I have returned!"

There was no response. Deep quiet held the house. Turjan wished he were in the open air where the odor of sorcery was less strong. He looked at the doors; one led to the entrance hall, the other he knew not where. The door on the right hand must lead outside; he laid his hand on the latch to pull it open. But he paused. Suppose he were mistaken, and Pandelume's form were revealed? Would it be wiser to wait here?

A solution occurred to him. His back to the door, he swung it open.

"Pandelume!" he called.

A soft intermittent sound came to his ears from behind, and he seemed to hear a labored breath. Suddenly frightened, Turjan stepped back into the circular room and closed the door.

He resigned himself to patience and sat on the floor.

A gasping cry came from the next room. Turjan leapt to his feet.

"Turjan? You are there?"

"Yes; I have returned with the amulet."

"Do this quickly," panted the voice. "Guarding your

sight, hang the amulet over your neck and enter."

Turjan, spurred by the urgency of the voice, closed his eyes and arranged the amulet on his chest. He groped to the door and flung it wide.

Silence of a shocked intensity held an instant; then came an appalling screech, so wild and demoniac that Turjan's brain sang. Mighty pinions buffeted the air, there was a hiss and the scrape of metal. Then, amidst muffled roaring, an icy wind bit Turjan's face. Another hiss—and all was quiet.

"My gratitude is yours," said the calm voice of Pandelume. "Few times have I experienced such dire stress, and without your aid might not have repulsed that creature of hell."

A hand lifted the amulet from Turjan's neck. After a moment of silence Pandelume's voice sounded again from a distance.

"You may open your eyes."

Turjan did so. He was in Pandelume's workroom; amidst much else, he saw vats like his own.

"I will not thank you," said Pandelume. "But in order that a fitting symmetry be maintained, I perform a service for a service. I will not only guide your hands as you work among the vats, but also will I teach you other matters of value."

In this fashion did Turjan enter his apprenticeship to Pandelume. Day and far into the opalescent Embelyon night he worked under Pandelume's unseen tutelage. He learned the secret of renewed youth, many spells of the ancients, and a strange abstract lore that Pandelume termed "Mathematics."

"Within this instrument," said Pandelume, "resides the Universe. Passive in itself and not of sorcery, it elucidates every problem, each phase of existence, all the secrets of time and space. Your spells and runes are built upon its power and codified according to a great underlying mosaic of magic. The design of this mosaic we cannot surmise; our knowledge is didactic, empirical, arbitrary. Phandaal glimpsed the pattern and so was able to formulate many of the spells which bear his name. I have endeavored through the ages to break the clouded glass, but so far my research has failed. He who discovers the pattern will know all of sorcery and be a man powerful beyond comprehension."

So Turjan applied himself to the study and learned many of the simpler routines.

"I find herein a wonderful beauty," he told Pandelume. "This is no science, this is art, where equations fall away to elements like resolving chords, and where always prevails a symmetry either explicit or multiplex, but always of a crystalline serenity."

In spite of these other studies, Turjan spent most of his time at the vats, and under Pandelume's guidance achieved the mastery he sought. As a recreation he formed a girl of exotic design, whom he named Floriel. The hair of the girl he had found with Kandive on the night of the festival had fixed in his mind, and he gave his creature pale green hair. She had skin of creamy tan and wide emerald eyes. Turjan was intoxicated with delight when he brought her wet and perfect from the vat. She learned quickly and soon knew how to speak with Turjan. She was one of dreamy and wistful habit, caring for little but wandering among the flowers of the meadow, or sitting silently by the river; yet she was a pleasant creature and her gentle manners amused Turjan.

But one day the black-haired T'sais came riding past on her horse, steely-eyed, slashing at flowers with her sword. The innocent Floriel wandered by and T'sais, exclaiming "Green-eyed woman—your aspect horrifies me, it is death for you!" cut her down as she had the flowers in her path.

Turjan, hearing the hooves, came from the workroom in time to witness the sword-play. He paled in rage and a spell of twisting torment rose to his lips. Then T'sais looked at him and cursed him, and in the pale face and dark eyes he saw her misery and the spirit that caused her to defy her fate and hold to her life. Many emotions fought in him, but at last he permitted T'sais to ride on. He buried Floriel by the river-bank and tried to forget her in intense study.

A few days later he raised his head from his work.

"Pandelume! Are you near?"

"What do you wish, Turjan?"

"You mentioned that when you made T'sais, a flaw warped her brain. Now I would create one like her, of the same intensity, yet sound of mind and spirit."

"As you will," replied Pandelume indifferently, and gave Turjan the pattern.

So Turjan built a sister to T'sais, and day by day watched the same slender body, the same proud features take form.

When her time came, and she sat up in her vat, eyes glowing with joyful life, Turjan was breathless in haste to help her forth.

She stood before him wet and naked, a twin to Tsais, but where the face of T'sais was racked by hate, here dwelt peace and merriment; where the eyes of T'sais glowed with fury, here shone the stars of imagination.

Turjan stood wondering at the perfection of his own creation. "Your name shall be T'sain," said he, "and already I know that you will be part of my life."

He abandoned all else to teach T'sain, and she learned with marvelous speed.

"Presently we return to Earth," he told her, "to my home beside a great river in the green land of Ascolais."

"Is the sky of Earth filled with colors?" she inquired.

"No," he replied. "The sky of Earth is a fathomless dark blue, and an ancient red sun rides across the sky. When night falls the stars appear in patterns that I will teach you. Embelyon is beautiful, but Earth is wide, and the horizons extend far off into mystery. As soon as Pandelume wills, we return to Earth."

T'sain loved to swim in the river, and sometimes Turjan came down to splash her and toss rocks in the water while he dreamed. Against T'sais he had warned her, and she had promised to be wary.

But one day, as Turjan made preparations for departure, she wandered far afield through the meadows, mindful only of the colors at play in the sky, the majesty of the tall blurred trees, the changing flowers at her feet;

she looked on the world with a wonder that is only for those new from the vats. Across several low hills she wandered, and through a dark forest where she found a cold brook. She drank and sauntered along the bank, and presently came upon a small dwelling.

The door being open, T'sain looked to see who might live here. But the house was vacant, and the only furnishings were a neat pallet of grass, a table with a basket of nuts, a shelf with a few articles of wood and pewter.

T'sain turned to go on her way, but at this moment she heard the ominous thud of hooves, sweeping close like fate. The black horse slid to a stop before her. T'sain shrank back in the doorway, all Turjan's warnings returning to her mind. But T'sais had dismounted and came forward with her sword ready. As she raised to strike, their eyes met, and T'sais halted in wonder.

It was a sight to excite the brain, the beautiful twins, wearing the same white waist-high breeches, with the same intense eyes and careless hair, the same slim pale bodies, the one wearing on her face hate for every atom of the universe, the other a gay exuberance.

T'sais found her voice.

"How is this, witch? You bear my semblance, yet you are not me. Or has the boon of madness come at last to dim my sight of the world?"

T'sain shook her head. "I am T'sain. You are my twin, T'sais, my sister. For this I must love you and you must love me."

"Love? I love nothing! I will kill you and so make the world better by one less evil." She raised her sword again.

"No!" cried T'sain in anguish. "Why do you wish to harm me? I have done no wrong!"

"You do wrong by existing, and you offend me by coming to mock my own hideous mold."

T'sain laughed. "Hideous? No. I am beautiful, for Turjan says so. Therefore you are beautiful, too."

T'sais' face was like marble.

"You make sport of me."

"Never. You are indeed very beautiful."

T'sais dropped the point of her sword to the ground. Her face relaxed into thought.

"Beauty! What is beauty! Can it be that I am blind, that a fiend distorts my vision? Tell me, how does one see beauty?"

"I don't know," said T'sain. "It seems very plain to me. Is not the play of colors across the sky beautiful?"

T'sais looked up in astonishment. "The harsh glarings? They are either angry or dreary, in either case detestable."

"See how delicate are the flowers, fragile and charming."

"They are parasites, they smell vilely."

T'sain was puzzled. "I do not know how to explain beauty. You seem to find joy in nothing. Does nothing give you satisfaction?"

"Only killing and destruction. So then these must be beautiful."

T'sain frowned. "I would term these evil concepts."

"Do you believe so?"

"I am sure of it."

T'sais considered. "How can I know how to act? I have been certain, and now you tell me that I do evil!"

T'sain shrugged. "I have lived little, and I am not wise. Yet I know that everyone is entitled to life. Turjan could explain to you easily."

"Who is Turjan?" inquired T'sais.

"He is a very good man," replied T'sain, "and I love him greatly. Soon we go to Earth, where the sky is vast and deep and of dark blue."

"Earth . . . If I went to Earth, could I also find beauty and love?"

"That may be, for you have a brain to understand beauty, and beauty of your own to attract love."

"Then I kill no more, regardless of what wickedness I see. I will ask Pandelume to send me to Earth."

T'sain stepped forward, put her arms around T'sais, and kissed her.

"You are my sister and I will love you."

T'sais' face froze. Rend, stab, bite, said her brain, but a deeper surge welled up from her flowing blood, from every cell of her body, to suffuse her with a sudden flush of pleasure. She smiled.

"Then—I love you, my sister. I kill no more, and I will find and know beauty on Earth or die."

T'sais mounted her horse and set out for Earth, seeking love and beauty.

T'sain stood in the doorway, watching her sister ride off through the colors. Behind her came a shout, and Turjan approached.

"T'sain! Has that frenzied witch harmed you?" He did not wait for a reply. "Enough! I kill her with a spell, that she may wreak no more pain."

He turned to voice a terrible charm of fire, but T'sain put her hand to his mouth.

"No, Turjan, you must not. She has promised to kill no more. She goes to Earth seeking what she may not find in Embelyon."

So Turjan and T'sain watched T'sais disappear across the many-colored meadow.

"Turjan," spoke T'sain.

"What is your wish?"

"When we come to Earth, will you find me a black horse like that of T'sais?"

"Indeed," said Turjan, laughing, as they started back to the house of Pandelume.

Narnian Suite

IF THIS anthology seems a trifle top-heavy in favor of American writers of the imaginary world fantasy over their British colleagues, it is probably the result of the enormous rise of popular fiction magazines in this country which provided broad markets for American fantasy. But there was no lacuna in the British tradition: in fact, the dates of the major British authors in the genre overlap.

William Morris died in 1896; E. R. Eddison in 1945; Lord Dunsany in 1957. The next important British novelist in this field, C. S. Lewis, was born in 1898 and died in 1963. In other words, Lewis was 47 when Eddison died and 59 when Dunsany died. And he himself was contemporary to J. R. R. Tolkien (1892–); in fact, they were professional colleagues and the best of friends.

Clive Staples Lewis was a keenly intelligent, brilliantly imaginative and wonderfully articulate gentleman. He wrote something like thirty books in all, and among them are a number of excellent fantasies which are of interest to the readers of this anthology. During his heyday he was the center of a small, congenial group of authors and intellectuals who called themselves "the Inklings." They gathered informally in Lewis' rooms at Magdalen College every Thursday evening after dinner to talk of "beer, Beowulf, torture, Tertullian, bores, the contractual theory of medieval kingship, odd place-names" and anything else of interest. Among them were John Wain, David

Cecil, the fantasy novelist and poet Charles Williams, W. H. Lewis (C. S. Lewis' brother, also a writer) and Professor Tolkien.

The Inklings formed the habit of reading aloud from their current works-in-progress. Thus Lewis and his friends enjoyed the amazing privilege of hearing *The Lord of the Rings* read aloud from the original manuscript by its author. Lewis was one of the first enthusiasts of Tolkien's masterpiece; he helped get *The Hobbit* into print, and when *LOTR* was being published, he gave it a glowing, heart-felt review in *Time and Tide*, saying:

"Here are beauties which pierce like swords or burn like cold iron; here is a book that will break your heart . . . good beyond hope."

The review was tremendously influential. Tolkien had published a few critical studies, and the children's book *The Hobbit*, but he was still known primarily as an Oxford don. But Lewis, at this time, was a world-famous author, poet, essayist, and a distinguished lay theologian, then at the very height of his fame, a writer of international repute and a major critic.

Among his fiction is at least one modern classic, *The Screwtape Letters*, which will doubtless outlive us all. He also wrote a strange and wonderful science fiction trilogy composed of *Out of the Silent Planet*, *Perelandra* and *That Hideous Strength*, unique in that it combines theology and occultism with science fiction. And in the genre of the imaginary world, he produced what is probably a lasting contribution to the world's small shelf of authentic fantasy classics for children, the seven slim novels that make up the Chronicles of Narnia.

Narnia is one of the most interesting fantasy worlds known to me. Again, Lewis has blended theology, occultism and fantasy into a unique fictional experience. The god of Narnia is Aslan the talking lion—a linguistic pun: the Persian word for "lion" is *arslan*. We observe as the lion god "sings" Narnia into creation. Elsewhere in the series, Aslan suffers a type of crucifixion, and returns to life. Amidst these more serious matters move a delightful host of interesting characters, Giants, Fauns, Dwarves,

Dancing Trees and Talking Beasts (such as the inimitable and gallant Reepicheep, a murine D'Artagnan, and my personal favorite, doubtless the most heroic mouse in literature).

I wanted a sample of C. S. Lewis' imaginary world fantasy for this anthology, but had some difficulties finding anything. His few short stories are not in this genre, and, short of taking a chapter out of one of the Narnia books, I could find nothing for *The Young Magicians*.

Luckily, I found a Narnian *poem*! It is not taken from one of the books, but appeared on its own in *Punch* in the issue for November 4, 1953. I am sure most of my readers will not have read it . . . .

---

*

1

*March for Strings, Kettledrums,
and Sixty-three Dwarfs*

With plucking pizzicato and the prattle of the
    Kettledrum
We're trotting into battle mid a clatter of accoutrement;
Our beards are big as periwigs and trickle with
    opopanax,
And trinketry and treasure twinkle out on every part of
    us—
     (Scrape! Tap! The fiddle and the kettledrum).

The chuckle-headed humans think we're only petty
    poppetry
And all our battle-tackle nothing more than pretty
    bric-a-brac;
But a little shrub has prickles, and they'll soon be in a
    pickle if
A scud of dwarfiish archery has crippled all their
    cavalry—
     (Whizz! Twang! The quarrel and the javelin).

And when the tussle thickens we can writhe and wriggle
    under it;
Then dagger-point'll tickle 'em, and grab and grip'll
    grapple 'em,
And trap and trick'll trouble 'em and tackle 'em and
    topple 'em
Till they're huddled, all be-diddled, in the middle of our
    caperings—
      (Dodge! Jump! The wriggle and the summer-
      sault).

When we've scattered 'em and peppered 'em with
    pebbles from our catapults
We'll turn again in triumph and by crannies and by
    crevices
Go back to where the capitol and cradle of our people is,
Our forges and our furnaces, the caverns of the earth—
      (Gold! Fire! The anvil and the smithying).

2

March for Drum, Trumpet, and Twenty-one Giants
    With stumping stride in pomp and pride
    We come to thump and floor ye;
    We'll bump your lumpish heads to-day
    And tramp your ramparts into clay,
    And as we stamp and romp and play
    Our trump'll blow before us—
  (*Crescendo*) Oh tramp it, tramp it, tramp it, trumpet,
  trumpet blow before us!

    We'll grind and break and bind and take
    And plunder ye and pound ye!
    With trundled rocks and bludgeon blow,
    You dunderheads, we'll dint ye so
    You'll blunder and run blind, as though
    By thunder stunned, around us—
  By thunder, thunder, thunder, thunder stunned around
  us!

Ho! tremble town and tumble down
And crumble shield and sabre!
Your kings will mumble and look pale,
Your horses stumble or turn tail,
Your skimble-scamble counsels fail,
So rumble drum belaboured—
(*Diminuendo*) Oh rumble, rumble, rumble, rumble,
rumble drum belaboured!

Once Upon A Time
and
The Dragon's Visit

THE 20th Century has produced many fantasy novels of power, brilliance, ingenuity, and even authentic genius. Among the best published in this century I would list Cabell's *Jurgen*, White's *The Sword in the Stone*, Merritt's *Dwellers in the Mirage*, Eddison's *The Worm Ouroboros*, Dunsany's *The King of Elfland's Daughter*, Pratt's *The Well of the Unicorn*, Vance's *The Dying Earth*, Finney's *The Circus of Doctor Lao*, Peake's *Titus Groan* and David Lindsay's *A Voyage to Arcturus*. But any knowledgeable enthusiast in the field will have his own list of favorites.

Out of all the fantasies written in this century, *The Lord of the Rings* is the greatest, beyond all question. Professor Tolkien's magnificent three-part super-novel is the single most magnificent masterpiece in fantasy literature. In breadth of conception, depth of characterization, scope of imagination, it stands alone.

J. R. R. (for John Ronald Reuel) Tolkien was born in Bloemfontein, Union of South Africa, on January 3, 1892, of British parentage and German descent. He was only three or four when his father died and his mother brought Tolkien and his brother back to her birthplace,

Birmingham, in northwestern Warwickshire, England. Tolkien studied at Exeter College in Oxford, served with the Lancashire Fusiliers during World War One, and eventually became Rawlinson and Bosworth Professor of Anglo-Saxon at Pembroke College, Oxford. He published studies of Chaucer and *Beowulf*, a Middle-English vocabulary and various other translations and scholarly papers.

He was, of course, not the first Oxford don to publish fantasy novels. A certain Charles Lutwidge Dodgson preceded him by many years, with something called *Alice's Adventure in Wonderland*. But out of his scholarly interest in linguistics came a beautiful invented language, Elvish, and out of this evolved an imaginary world, Middle-earth, wherein such a language might be spoken: from this, in time, came the most brilliant fantasy masterpiece of our century.

I am not going to discuss Tolkien at any length. I presume that most of my readers will already be familiar with his work. And, for those who are not, I have written a full-length book about the Professor and his work, a study called *Tolkien: A Look Behind "The Lord of the Rings"* (Ballantine, 1969).

As with C. S. Lewis, I was at a loss to find something by Professor Tolkien for this anthology. In Tolkien's case, my publishers already have in print virtually everything he has written save for his scholarly papers. Fortunately, the Professor has most kindly given me two new "Bombadil" poems, contributed especially for this anthology and never before printed in America.

I hope you will find them as charming as I do . . . .

———◆———

Once upon a day on the fields of May
there was snow in summer where the blossom lay;
the buttercups tall sent up their light
in a stream of gold, and wide and white
there opened in the green grass-skies

the earth-stars with their steady eyes
watching the Sun climb up and down.
Goldberry was there with a wild-rose crown,
Goldberry was there in a lady-smock
blowing away a dandelion clock,
stooping over a lily-pool
and twiddling the water green and cool
to see it sparkle round her hand:
once upon a time in elvish land.

Once upon a night in the cockshut light
the grass was grey but the dew was white;
shadows were dark, and the Sun was gone,
the earth-stars shut, but the high stars shone,
one to another winking their eyes
as they waited for the Moon to rise.
Up he came, and on leaf and grass
his white beams turned to twinkling glass,
and silver dripped from stem and stalk
down to where the lintips walk
through the grass-forests gathering dew.
Tom was there without boot or shoe,
with moonshine wetting his big, brown toes:
once upon a time, the story goes.

Once upon a moon on the brink of June
a-dewing the lintips went too soon.
Tom stopped and listened, and down he knelt:
'Ha! little lads! So it was you I smelt?
What a mousy smell! Well, the dew is sweet,
so drink it up, but mind my feet!'
The lintips laughed and stole away,
but old Tom said: 'I wish they'd stay!
The only things that won't talk to me,
say what they do or what they be.
I wonder what they have got to hide?
Down from the Moon maybe they slide,
or come in star-winks, I don't know':
Once upon a time and long ago.

The Dragon's Visit

THE FOLLOWING is a minor, though charming, example of Professor Tolkien's work. It cannot suggest either his range or his power or his extraordinary wealth of imaginative fertility: for those you must explore the world of *The Lord of the Rings*.

The first publication of that masterpiece, beginning in Great Britain in 1954, is likely to be remembered by connoisseurs of fantasy as a milestone, a major turning-point, marking the beginning of a new era. Fantasy can never quite be the same after Tolkien as it was before; every future writer who enters the genre of the imaginary world fantasy will be aware of Tolkien, just as every mountain-climber is aware of Sir Edmund Hillary and Tenzing Norkay. Whole generations of new writers will be influenced by Tolkien and will seek to emulate him, to learn from him, and will attempt to equal his achievement, just as Lovecraft and his circle were inspired by the achievements of Dunsany.

It is now only fifteen years since the first appearance of the Tolkien trilogy. Already, the signs of influence can be discerned among a whole new generation of fantasy writers who have begun publishing after that milestone date. Primarily, the Tolkien-influenced writers I have seen thus far have been writers of juvenile fiction, like Lloyd Alexander and his splendid "Prydain" novels, or Alan Garner's *The Weirdstone of Brisingamen* and its sequel, or Carol Kendall's *The Gammage Cup* and *The*

Whisper of Glocken, and a few others of comparable merit.

And, although every new work of fantasy to be published since 1954 or thereabouts is promptly labelled "Tolkienian" by publishers' bright young publicity men (with one eye on the sales department and the other on the coterie of book reviewers), I have not actually seen a work of book-length fiction, clearly for the adult reader, which displays the earmarks of having been influenced by Tolkien. However, it is only a matter of time . . .

This being the case, and since the sequential structure of this anthology is, roughly, at least, a chronological arrangement of representative authors prominent in the genre from William Morris down to Tolkien, I am left dangling for a final selection which would demonstrate the sort of fiction we might expect to enjoy "after Tolkien." I am, therefore, and with all due humility, including a segment from a work-in-progress of my own. This is done in lieu of an example from the work of another, and superior, writer, rather than from any confidence on my part that Lin Carter is worthy to be ranked with the titans from whose work the bulk of this anthology is drawn.

The extract is taken from the opening pages of a book which has been some ten years in the making thus far, and is still many years from completion. At that time, the work as a whole—whose estimated length I project as in the neighborhood of half a million words—will bear the title *Khymyrium: The City of a Hundred Kings, from the Coming of Aviathar the Lion to the Passing of Spheridion the Doomed*.

While it would be indecorous for me to claim any particular artistry or merit for this extract or its parent work, it has at least the feature of innovation. As readers of my book *Tolkien: A Look Behind "The Lord of the Rings"* will be aware, it is my theory that the so-called epic fantasy, or imaginary world fiction, basically employs either one of two basic plot-themes, or a combination of the two. These themes are the Quest (or Journey) and the War theme. The finest examples of the epic fantasy in recent literature, E. R. Eddison's *The Worm Ouroboros* and J. R. R. Tolkien's *The Lord of the Rings*, employ an adroit blending of both themes. For this projected novel of mine, written "after Tolkien," I resolved to discover yet a third plot-theme whereby epic fantasy might be written.

I found it at last in the Mythological History. The Persian epic poet Firdausi, for example, wrote a famous book called *Shah Namah*, or "the Book of the Kings." In this book, one of the world's most fascinating compilations, he organized the immense and diverse heroic and legendary literature and folklore of his native Persia into a chronological history which began with the creation of the world and the reign of early, prehistoric hero-kings and ended with known historical events like the Moslem conquest of his homeland.

Khymyrium will be such a book. It will cover one thousand years in the history of an imaginary world, and will largely concern itself with the founding, the rise, the wars, the zenith, the decline and the extinction of a world empire. Like a genuine history, it will have its footnotes, its scholarly appendices, its illustrations drawn from the sculpture, the tapestries, the murals and mosaics and paintings and numismatics of its imaginary world, Istradorpha.

The following brief extract relates the legend of the arrival in Sarthay and the Maremma (the site of the future Empire of Khymyrium) of the divine hero, Aviathar, who is to lay the foundations of the Empire and from whose loins will spring its race of world-conquering kings, armed with the charmed might and authority of a great Sword of Power . . . .

———◆———

On the cherry-trees the dragon lay
   a-simmering and a-dreaming.
The blossom was white in the early day,
   but green his scales were gleaming.
Over the seas he had flown by night,
   for his land was dragon-haunted,

Stuffed with gold and jewels bright,
  but food and sport he wanted.

'Excuse me, Mr. Higgins, please!
  Have you seen what's in your garden?
There's a dragon on your cherry-trees!'
  'A what? I beg your pardon!'
Mr. Higgins fetched the garden-hose,
  and the dragon woke from dreaming.
He blinked and snorted in his nose
  when he felt the water streaming.

'How cool!' he said. 'So good for scales!
  I did not expect a fountain!
I'll sit and sing here, till daylight fails
  and the full moon's mounting.'
But Higgins runs, on the doors he knocks
  of Miss Biggins and old Tupper.
'Come help me quick! Come, Mr. Box,
  or he'll eat us all for supper!'

Miss Biggins sent for the Fire Brigade
  with a long red ladder,
And a brave show their helmets made;
  but the dragon's heart grew sadder:
'It reminds me of the wicked ways
  of warriors unfeeling,
Hunting us in the bad old days
  and our bright gold stealing.'

The Captain with his hatchet came:
  'Now what d'you think you're doing?'
The dragon laughed: 'Cap'n What's-your-name,
  I'm sitting here and stewing.
I like to stew. So let me be!
  Or your church-steeple
I'll batter down, blast every tree,
  and you, and eat these people!'

'Turn on the hydrant!' said Captain George
  and down the ladder tumbled.

The dragon's eyes like coals in a forge
    glowed, and his belly rumbled.
He began to steam; he threshed his tail,
    and away the blossom fluttered.
But the Brigade were not the men to quail,
    although he growled and muttered.

With poles they jabbed him from below,
    where he was rather tender:
'Havoc!' the dragon cried, *'haro!'*
    and rose in splendour.
He smashed the town to a rubbish-heap,
    and over the Bay of Bimble
Sailors could see the red flames leap
    from Bumpus Head to Trimble.

The Higgins was tough, and as for Box:
    just like his name he tasted;
The dragon threw Tupper on the rocks,
    and said, 'This munching's wasted.'
So he buried the hatchet and Captain George,
    and he sang a dirge for Higgins
On a cliff above the long white shores—
    and he did not miss Miss Biggins.

Sadly he sang till the moon went down,
    with the surf below sighing
On the grey rocks, and in Bimbletown
    the red blaze dying.
He saw the peaks far over the sea
    round his own land ranging;
And he mused on Men, and how strange they be,
    and the old order changing.

None of them now have the wit to admire
    a dragon's song or colour,
Nor the nerve with steel to meet his fire—
    the world is getting duller!'
He spread his wide wings to depart;
    but just as he was rising

Miss Biggins stabbed him to the heart,
 and that he found surprising.

'I regret this very much,' she said.
 'You're a very splendid creature,
And your voice is quite remarkable
 for one who has had no teacher;
But wanton damage I will not have,
 I really had to end it.'
The dragon sighed before he died:
 'At least she called me splendid.'

Azlon

from Khymyrium, *a work-in-progress*

❖─◆─◆──◆─◆─◆───◆─◆─◆──◆─◆─◆─❖

*So he came up from Sardinak the City of the Sea, as had
been prophesied, to the place whereat the Jander greeteth
the rolling flood of Eryphon and joineth in the last league of
her long journey to the Sundering Sea.*

*And he found Glasgerd the Keep of that Gondomir who
was Lord of the lords of Sarthay. It lifted tall towers beside
the Two Rivers, and he begged guesting for the night, and
they admitted him, and he entered therein.*

And this also had been foretold aforetime . . .

*1. He Cometh Unto the
Keep of Gondomir*

THE ember-colored and westering Sun was poised atop
the Hills of Thald, and pearl-tinted mists came rolling
from the level floods over the River Road and down
across meadows of fragrant and darkling grasses.

It was the hour of Sun's Dying. Now athwart the
western skies, sunset unfolded her vast ensanguined
banners, as he came up the dusty road with the shadows
of evening lapping at his heels.

It looked to be a stormy night, for all the youth could see. Cold winds woke and moved in groves of hoary silverwood and there were a plenty of stormclouds stood high-piled against the east, struck with the last rays till they were empurpled as with the gore from some aerial battleground. Thunder growled deep-throated amongst the roiling clouds and the gusty air smelled of the coming of rain.

Hence he deemed him fortunate to have found this haven against the night which, by such tokens, should prove inhospitable to travellers.

The hooves of his horned stallion clottered hollowly over the wooden bridge that spanned the moat, and he dismounted at the Porte, stiff with weariness from his long hard hours in the saddle. And the archers stationed there, and the tall grey Captain of the Porte, gave him quiet greeting in the gathering shadows of the dusk.

*

Within the vast, smoky, cavernous hall of the keep, the Lord Gondomir sat this hour at table with two guests. Here, within, all was light and heat and smoke and roaring sound and bustle. A great fire blazed upon the broad stone hearth and its rich orange light sent huge shadows leaping and cavorting up the rough stone wall. This feasting-hall was built to kingly and heroic proportions: the arched roof above was lost to view amidst thick-clotted shadow, and it was raised and supported by tremendous columns of massy stone like to great trees in their girth. Sputtering torches, clamped against stone walls in brackets of grim black iron, cast forth thick gold light. They were set between worn tapestries of olden-work, which pictured forth in shades of umber, green, dull red and golden-brown, familiar scenes of hunt and siege and battle, the high deeds of heroes and famous amours of the Taosar.

Upon a raised dais of smooth greenish stone was set a mighty table or trestle of old black wood, shapen crescentiform; and upon this there was spread a noble feast of smoking meats and succulent pastries, ruddy fruit in

owls of gleaming brass, platters of seed-cakes drowned
in pungent spiced gravy, and great cups of foaming
brown ale or heady wines cooled in the swift waters of
Jander.

At this table were seated three men, differing greatly
in age, station and raiment. There was a small, spry,
birdlike little seer with thin white nervous hands and
sharp black eyes that flickered here and there with keen
inquisitiveness. He had a round bald skull that gleamed
like a globe of polished ivory, and it was bare save for a
cap of red satin worn against the night-chills. From the
full, voluminous canonicals of mystic purple wherein he
was robed, you would have known him for a member of
the Holy Brotherhood of Augurs, sworn and dedicated to
the Taos Sarganastor the Patron of Magic and Prophecy.
This was His Purity, Chelian, Abbot of Thax, taken by
night on the road to seacoast Islarch Keroona, thither-
bound for consultation with the Speaking Stone.

Opposite from this Chelian sat a tall brown saturnine
man of thirty or more winters, stout-clad in a long byrny
of fine link-steel cleverly interworked with the cunning
of the Gnarly-smiths: the whole washed in liquid gold,
and interset with cut bezoars that burned like hot brown
tars. The face of this man was gaunt and harsh and
famished. His eyes were black, dull, opaque, and yet
sly and disquietingly a-lit. He had a tight grim mouth
framed with a stiff coarse spade-beard of black which
was shot through and through with rough patches of
grey. His head was clothed in soft black felt, draped in
intricate folds and escalloped where it fell close about his
brows. A great axe hung at his waist by leathern thongs.

This was the famed war-captain, the Twice-Valiant
Lynxias, and he was come from Phome Against the Ny-
ainian Hills, bound for the lustral Games.

Between these two, in a mighty thronelike chair of ancient ironwood all worked and carved with the likenesses of Gnarly-folk and Firedrakes and the Ops and
other beasts, sat their host, the Lord Gondomir of Glas-
erd Keep, first among the Twelve Barons who hold all
this Forest Kingdom of Sarthay as their domain.

This Lord Gondomir was a stout, full-bodied man well past the zenith of his years, huge and bearded and blustering. In the high bright days of his warlike youth he had captained the Levy of Sarthay, and his deeds were not neglected by the makers of songs. It was told how that they marched against Sea Rovers come a-slaving from the Isles Gorgonian and broke the howling Islanders in day-long battle at Falgalon field. And how, betimes, he led the host up against the Wild Men of the Grey Hills, who go a-bearded and maned like beasts, and fight with a beast's ferocity, but with clubs of stone only, for they eschew the bronzen weaponry of city-folk. They said that even at this day, well past his prime, he towered among other warriors like a great bull among calves, or a mighty ram striding amongst the ewes—which saying was most apt for that his blazon was an ram's-head, black, on a silvern field.

Such was Gondomir of Glasgerd Keep: rough of manner and rude of speech, his converse peppery with all kind of coarse and barbarous oaths, gruff in his temper as a growling bear; and yet, withal, wise in his counsels and great-of-heart. His hand lay lightly on the rod of power, and his people loved him.

The Lord Gondomir was bellowing just now, roaring in his rude and hearty humor over some slight witticism passed by the little Augur. The Lord threw back his grey-maned head, his massive chest and shoulders quaking with mirth until the table quivered with the peals of his ringing laughter. His bluff, ruddy face, craggy-featured with keen good eyes sharp under tufted brows, beamed with jovial good humor, and candor, and fiery quick temper. His girth was robed in bottle-green and apricot velvet, much stained about the chest with meat and wine, trimmed at throat and cuff and hem with grey fur the color of his beard. The brave Seal of Sarthay flashed on the thumb of his great scarred hand and the Black Ram of Glasgerd was worked into the fabric of these robes where they were bound across his deep chest.

And around his throat upon an heavy chain of rosy orichalc, thick-set with yellow zircons that gleamed and glistened like transparent gold, hung the Order of the Gold Wyvern. It flashed, catching the firelight as he laughed.

Thus was Gondomir, as we see him first.

2. Of His Entering-In,
And of His Seeming

To THE Baron there came bent white-bearded old Cresper, the steward of the Keep, leaning on the silver-shod staff of his office. He bowed stiff-backed and spake, saying there awaited my Lord's pleasure without a warrior-lad who begged shelter for this night against the gathering storm. And even as the old man spake, wind shrieked about the tower and they within heard hollow thunder go gobbling down the sky and there flickered past the tall and peaked windows a sheet of lightning like a golden wing quick-spread and then back-folded.

"Know we this warrior?" the Lord demanded.

"I think not, my Lord. He is one Aviathar by name," the old steward quavered.

"Well, what doth he bear?"

"A lion's face in full, gold, on a field crimson," Cresper made reply.

Gondomir frowned, wrinkling-up his heavy brow. He turned in inquiry to his guest, the war-captain Lynxias.

"Know you aught of such bearings, friend?"

"Nay; a blazon strange to me, my Lord," the captain said. Gondomir thence turned to his other guest.

"Your Purity?"

The bald little Abbot twitched thin shoulders in a shrug. "Equal-strange to me, as well, Lord Gondomir. An Augur, I, and no Herald. But . . . face-in-full? A Cydacian blazon, perchance?"

A mighty gust of wind shouted beyond the stout walls and loosed a heavy torrent of rain to crash thunderously against the steep-vaulted roof of the hall. The storm no longer impended, but was come in its fury.

"Well," the Baron said heartily, "though we know this man not and he cometh hence in mystery, he may be a painted savage out of Barbaria for all I care. Nay; I would not forbid guest-right to a demon come glibbering up from the deepest pit of Tazenderzath the Abyss of Fire, on such a night as this bodes well to be! Admit the stranger-knight, Cresper; he be welcome to this board, so he cometh to it in peace and good-fellowship."

The steward bowed with slow dignity and withdrew, hobbling on his staff. And the Lord of Glasgerd Keep and his two guests ceased from their doings to turn curious eyes to see what manner and breed of visitor the storm had belched up against their gates.

Old Cresper returned forthwith and led into the smoky and cavernous immensity of the fire-lit hall a young man still in the springtide of his days, and fair-seeming, for all that he was much stained and bedraggled from travel, with boots grey with road-dust and a long, worn cloak stiff with sea-salt. The youth was led before his host, whereupon he bowed in greeting.

"Peace to this hall and to all therein," he said in a strong and quiet voice of deep timbre. "I am hight Aviathar, the son of Thamshyd of Memnos, a stranger but new-come to these lands about, but come in good-will."

From Memnos, then! The good Abbot Chelian, 'twould seem, had guessed shrewdly-well: yet herein lay a small puzzlement. For old Memnos-town lay far and farther still from forest-clad Sarthay, beyond the coast-lands and across the narrow, stormy waters of the Sundering Sea that cleft all of this land in twain from north to south; indeed, it lay in the land of Cydace Below Phasia, even as the Augur hazarded.

The puzzlement lay in the cause of so-far a journeying. For the time of the coming-forth of Aviathar out of Cydace lay in the first years of the Seventh Millenium of the World. And in these troublous and now-darkening years few journeyed from afar withouten good reason. For the harsh and warlike Princes of the Four Cities of

the Surna were even now a-casting covetous eyes upon
the rich realms of the south, and rumors of coming war
perturbed the Oracles. And from the gloom of The Dubious Land, beyond the Rivers, the ominous shadow of
The Woman spread slowly out of the Maremma to
over-lay the eastward marches of the Forest Kingdoms
with grim witcheries and unwholesome magics. In these
uneasy and contentious times, the tale repeateth, few
men ventured so far afield lacking good and solid rea-
son-why. For all this portion of the World's West was
sparse-settled by men and but newly-tamed by the Sons
of the Children of Thlunlarna, come hither from the
rocky shores of the Ultimate North but three centuries
agone, driven from their ancient homes by the will of
the August and Eternal Taosar to whelm the Gnarly-folk
and claim the West for the Kindred of Men. Much wilderness there was and empty land, to speak nothing of
great Eogrymgol itself, the Wood of the West, and the
cities of men were far-between and few in number;
wherewith also the roads that stretched betwixt them
were but ill-guarded and made perilous by the many
rogues and men of outlawry that had fallen betimes into
banditry and theft. In truth these were dark days when
no man felt truly secure and many yielded unto desperation, or had come into the fell service of The Woman.

Hence it was natural that the old Baron bent a shrewd
and measuring gaze upon the youth that stood before
him, to see that he admit under his roof no sly, outland-
ish reaver, for against such the hand of every man was
set and guest-right was a-forfeit.

Dathgold, the last-born son of Gondomir, the child of
the fullness of his age, was at these times scarce more
than a lad. Thus was he present, serving his sire among the
pages of the hall, as was the custom. And in his later
years, when that he was one of the Companions of
Thamshyd the King, he caused to be set down a word-
ketch of this first meeting of the Lords Gondomir and
Aviathar, whereof he was eye-witness. And we have thus
a portrait of him of Memnos as he looked in the springtide of his days, before even the hand of greatness

touched upon him first, and that but lightly, in the lists of Fontavery Downs, that later was to lay upon him full when the red Sun glowered down across the heavy-laden Field of Zolthak Koldah and all men hailed him Lord of Maremma.

Thus sayeth the memoir of Dathgold: the youth, Aviathar, was somewhat beneath the common height and lean of body, with that silken, sinewy length of limb whose lack of girth is deceptive unto the eye, concealing (as in your dancer, or your acrobat) an iron, an enduring, and an unyielding strength that breaks, but will not bend.

Of feature, he was small and regular and well-set, being neither handsome nor homely. His face was dark with wind and Sun. Hair, black as coal and coarse as a stallion's mane, brushed back lion-like from a broad, firm brow, and hacked off to shoulder-length. He had, as well, leonine, amberous eyes, strange to see in his dark visage, and grim-set under frowning brows of black.

They say he spake little, smiled seldom, laughed never.

The keen eyes of Gondomir studied him, and liked what they saw, for the stranger-knight was seemly and modest of manner, of mien grave yet courteous, and he bore withal the air of one who keeps his own counsels, observes much and thinks deeply.

His raiment was plain, much worn and frayed, withouten aught of ostentatious show: a simple leathern tunic to mid-thigh, all over-sewn with fish-like, overlapping bronzen scales; and this belted at waist with a broad leather girdle set with octogon-plates of steel. His helm, doffed in honor of his host, as was custom, was of plain worn iron, unadorned by plume nor gaud; of olden-make but not of Gnarly-work, in style antique, for the *orium*, the eye-shield, swept back in a rising curve off the brow to either side like unto thick blunt horns.

He bore a long, oval shield such as they fashion in Babdorna, a buckler whose light frame of supple, tough wood, overwhich was tight-stretched seasoned and heavy-lacquered leather afastened with rivets of red copper.

was worn close-strapped to the left forearm. Upon it his blazon caught the fireglow, the *diomus*, the lion's face, set forth in fresh gold, snarling fangs bared in menace, the eyes picked out in crimson, and the whole framed with the tangled locks of the mane spread out in a jag-edged ruff upon a blood-red field.

The Abbot Chelian, who has also left unto us his memoir of this famous meeting, albeit principally of the Round of Converse thereafter, bent upon the youth the clear, keen scrutiny of his quick glance. It is recorded that he, too, liked well what he saw in the face and manly person of the young Aviathar. There was something about him who was not yet known as the Lion of Memnos that made a deep impress upon all who looked upon him . . . a glamour of majesty, perchance; or a radiance of force, like the nigh-tangible and thrilling aura that beats about a princely magician when he goes Enstarred with Power. Mayhap it was some fore-hint of that rare glory yet to come upon him, which, like the dawning Sun ere it be full-risen over the horizon-edge of the World yet sheds a brilliant forecast of its coming splendor that lights the skies before it. The boy Dathgold strove to set this feeling down, and his words are these: "Somewhat there was, whether in his ready and warlike stance, or in the lion-like, impassive and fiery topaz of his eyes (which burned slumberous, steady, unwinking, very like unto the eyes of a great beast), or whatever, none can quite say; but it caused a certain stillness within you, as if you stood in the presence of sheathed and unawakened mightiness."

3. He Joineth Them at Table
and Meeteth the Lords

THIS GONDOMIR, a shrewd and goodly judge of men, summed him up with a single long and lingering glance. A landless youth of barren purse, withouten name or fame, yet sprung perchance from some family of the lesser nobilities or the gentry of the minor Keeps, so he reckoned; and mayhap faring forth to seek fortune in service to a foreign prince.

In very truth, the young Aviathar was but little more than this. His seeming did not belie him: unprepossessing in appearance; in manner, withdrawn and somber; from his poor and worn accouterments, impoverished.

But strapped across his back in a worn scabbard of black leather there slept a mighty glaive, a Sword of Power, even that blade men name Azlon the Great, which goeth not unremembered by the bards nor forgotten by the chroniclers of high heroic deeds upon the earth of Istradorpha.

Thus Gondomir relaxed his suspicionings, and spake affably, and bade the youth be welcome in his hall, and roared to the pages to set another place.

"But, come, I do forget mine other guests," he said in his rough and hearty way. "I fear me you will think us rude unmannerly folk in this Forest Kingdom. Young sir, let me make known to you His Purity, Chelian, Abbot of Thax, and His Valiance, Lynxias of Phome, a mighty captain and twice-champion, far-famed alike on battlefield or tourney-ground. Come, sit you now, and sample our rough fare; will you join me in the demolishment of this haunch of meat? And yonder cup needs brimming—ho, Scather, you young rascal, wine for all!"

Aviathar yea-said him, and that with a right good will, and touched his brow in respectful salute to the Purple

Seer, which was acknowledged with a courteous nod and a birdlike flutter of quick, small hands, and to the captain, a warrior's greeting he bade, which the grim Lynxias returned with a muttered word or two. The young knight took his place at the board, seated at one horn of the crescent-shapen table without further ado.

And it was in this wise, the tale telleth, came Aviathar the Lion of Memnos unto Glasgerd Keep beside the Two Rivers in the land of Sarthay of the Forests . . .

❋

The pages, and Dathgold among them, set before him a great slab of steaming venison and filled his cup with foam-beaded ale, and he fell to with naught more of ceremony save that he spilt the first sip into the rushes in homage to the Divine Taosar, the Gods of Tethradoranderdon Mount, as was custom.

He was, in very sooth, famished, for his purse was as lean as his belly and he had eaten naught all that long day's riding up from Sardinak. Even had he chanced to own a coin to spend, he had come upon neither town nor castle keep wherein to spend it for the length of all the hard and dusty River Road that wendeth hither from that tall City of the Sea where galleons from far and fabled lands unlade their spicy bales and burthens, and whereat he had come a-land from his voyage by ship from seven-gated Lisimbra over-sea. And thus the rich steak, a-weltering in spiced gravy and sharp with curious herbs fetched out of savage Tharsha, was a Gods'-gift to his belly, over-long accustomed to narrow times and bleak road-fare.

When that his first hunger was somewhat appeased, he made thanks to the Lord for his graciousness, and said: "The sight of your fair and stout-walled Keep was full welcome, my Lord, for night betook me on the road still lacking by an league or more of my goal."

"Whither-bound, then, young sir?" asked Gondomir.

"To the Games of Sarthay," Aviathar made answer. "I had hoped to find an inn, or else to reach jasper-roofed

Thios-town ere the night came down. But the road was new and strange to me and I do fear I strayed overmuch from the short and swiftest way."

The Baron nodded affably. These Games were held each lustrum at a different field within the Forest Kingdom, and the fame of the great tourney or passage of arms was spread afar throughout the wide-wayed world. And, indeed, he might have guessed the young knight's goal, for what more wise a way for a warrior of such youthfulness, and doubtless yet untried in battle, to begin his quest of fame than by achieving some measure of victory at the great Games? It was even as the Rhapsode Kondorgrim sayeth in his versicle:

> *What life worth living does not point its prow*
> *Over the dark, endragoned, storm-wracked sea*
> *Unto the gold and gleaming coasts of Fame?*

"Aye," he said congenially, "stray you did indeed, and more, for Thios of the Jasper Roofs lieth a half-day's hard-riding from my Keep of Glasgerd here, and beyond the Hills of Thald, deep amidst the Shaws. You should have taken Samper-road an half-league back, for that it leadeth far and straight-away to Fontavary Downs amid the Dales. And 'tis there that we convene the Games this five-year. But no worry, for my lord Lynxias, here, rideth thither on the morrow, hoping to add yet an third bronzen chaplet to the twain he hath already won, the first at Chond Tivary five years agone, and t'other at Yoster Aspernvale this ten years since. As well, myself and sons and daughter, too, will hence with dawn. Doubtless, my lords, we shall all go forth together, with the day."

Aviathar thanked him for this courtesy. "And His Purity? Rideth he to the Games as well?" The small Abbot gave him a twinkling glance.

"Nay, no contender-for-chaplets I, young sir!" quoth he with a prim slight smile. "We of the Purple strive in more subtle, and, 'tis certain-sure, less temporal fields for the victor's wreath. Nay, my small skills lie in those adumbrative and fore-shadowing arts of divination that the display of martial prowess. I, then, for Islarch Keroona on the morn; thither to-morrow am I bound on a mission for my Brethren to consult the Oracle of the Stone, concerning some certain disquieting and ominous portents the Seers of the Purple have of late observed . . ."

Gondomir fanned the air with huge scarred strong hands.

"Come, come, my lords! Time enough for all such matters when we are done with meat—we shall have a Round of Converse with our wine when dinner's done: now we have yet to lay siege to these flower-cakes. My lord Abbot, I will have your opinion on them; we are far-famed for such pastries here in Sarthay. And my lord Lynxias! I do perceive me your cup is dry as The Waste. Scather, you empty-pate, fill up His Valiance's goblet to the brim!"

Aviathar bent again to the pleasant chore of appeasing his hunger, and he thought but little of the troubling words yonder Abbot had spoken. Neither did he observe that this Lynxias, who seemed surly and short-of-tongue, was, without so-seeming, subjecting him to a covert and searching scrutiny with fierce, shrewd, coldly speculating eyes . . .

Lynxias wondered, but was not sure, if this young stranger-knight was the one his Mistress had dispatched him here to intercept and murther in Eogrymgol Wood. But as for Chelian of Thax, the Abbot had no slightest inkling that this mild and seemly lad was the cause and center of those omens he was sent to query whereof with the Speaking Stone.

For not one of the three could guess or dream the might of this Aviathar, nor what his coming-hence into these lands did portend. That lay still in the unborn future.

A Basic Reading-List of Modern Heroic Fantasy

❖❖━❖━❖━❖━❖━❖━❖━❖━❖━❖❖

SOME of you may be new to the genre of the imaginary world fantasy, although I presume most of my writers will at least have read Professor Tolkien's books. For the benefit of those of you who are new to the field, and who perhaps would like to read more of this or that author, I have drawn up a brief bibliography of modern "Tolkienian" fantasy.

I have limited my selections to works only by the fourteen modern writers herein represented, and, since there is little point in recommending to your attention rare hardcover books out of print for decades, I list only those of their works published in American paperbacks during the past six or seven years—editions presumably still in print and still available.

WILLIAM MORRIS:

The Wood Beyond the World, Ballantine Books, 1969 The only one of Morris' several imaginary world fantasy novels still in print, and the first novel in this genre ever written. In The Ballantine Adult Fantasy Series.

Selected Writings and Designs (edited by Asa Briggs) Penguin Books, 1962. Contains a variety of Morris' essays critica, selections from his Socialist writings, quite a large amount of his poetry and some of his art.

LORD DUNSANY:

The King of Elfland's Daughter, Ballantine Books, 1969. The first Dunsany ever in paperback in this country, and the best of his fantasy novels. In The Ballantine Adult Fantasy Series.

The Edge of the World (edited by Lin Carter), Ballantine Books (forthcoming in 1970). Thirty of Dunsany's most brilliant fantasy stories selected from six of his short story collections. In The Ballantine Adult Fantasy Series.

E. R. EDDISON:

The Worm Ouroboros, Ballantine Books, 1967. The finest example of the imaginary world fantasy epic written before Tolkien, and a rousing and vigorous tale of quest, war and adventure told in rich, colorful, Elizabethan prose.

Mistress of Mistresses, Ballantine Books, 1967. The first novel of Eddison's Zimiamvia Trilogy, whose other volumes, *A Fish Dinner at Memison* and *The Mezentian Gate,* are also in print from the same publisher. But read the *Worm* first.

JAMES BRANCH CABELL:

Figures of Earth, Ballantine Books, 1969.

Jurgen, Avon Books, 1965. Probably the greatest fantasy novel ever written by an American, and a small classic of our literature.

The Silver Stallion, Ballantine Books, 1969. Read in this order, these three novels form a closely linked trilogy.

Figures and *Stallion* are in The Ballantine Adult Fantasy Series. More Cabell will be published in the Series in 1970.

H. P. LOVECRAFT:

The Dream Quest of Unknown Kadath, Ballantine Books (forthcoming in 1970). This is Lovecraft's only novel in the imaginary world genre; never before in paperback, it has been plumped out with several other stories written in his early "Dunsanian" style. In The Ballantine Adult Fantasy Series.

The Colour out of Space and Others, Lancer Books, 1967. Representative of Lovecraft's more popular and better known style, that of a master of supernatural horror. Contains some of his best-known stories, but no Tolkienian fantasy.

CLARK ASHTON SMITH:

Zothique (edited by Lin Carter), Ballantine Books (forthcoming in 1970). The first Smith book ever issued in paperback: a collection of all of his fantasies of the imaginary far future continent, Zothique. In The Ballantine Adult Fantasy Series.

A. MERRITT:

The Metal Monster, Avon Books, 1966.

The Ship of Ishtar, Avon Books, 1966.

Dwellers in the Mirage, Avon Books, 1967. Merritt carried on the tradition of the "lost race" novel from H. Rider Haggard, author of *She* and *King Solomon's Mines*, and with the exception of the single short story in this anthology, he wrote nothing that is strictly in the imaginary world genre. Still and all, he is a marvellous writer and his novels are tremendously entertaining. Start with *Dwellers*, my own favorite.

ROBERT E. HOWARD:

Conan the Conqueror, Lancer Books, 1967. Howard invented the sub-genre we call Sword & Sorcery, and this is his very best novel and a good one to start with.

King Kull (with Lin Carter), Lancer Books, 1967. An earlier series than the Conan yarns, about a savage warrior from primitive Atlantis who becomes king of an ancient realm. Completed by the present writer and never before in paperback.

Bran Mak Morn, Dell Books, 1969. More pre-Conan yarns, about an heroic prince of the Caledonian Picts and his battles against the invading legions of Rome. Splendid stuff.

ENRY KUTTNER:

The Dark World, Ace Books, 1965. A fine, old-fashioned adventure yarn written in the Merritt style.

The Well of the Worlds, Ace Books, 1965.

The Time Axis, Ace Books, 1965. These three novels are not really in the imaginary world genre, but very close to it. Kuttner wrote two series in the genre, the Elak of Atlantis series and the Prince Raynor stories (one of which is in this book), but neither has yet appeared in a volume of its own.

SPRAGUE DE CAMP:

The Tritonian Ring, Paperback Library, 1968. One of the best Sword & Sorcery novels yet written, and much in the vein of Robert E. Howard. Good swashbuckling adventure, livened with the delightful de Camp wit.

The Goblin Tower, Pyramid Books, 1968. A more serious and intelligent venture into the imaginary world genre, with less headlong heroics and more interesting characters. De Camp is one of the most brilliant of living fantasy writers.

Land of Unreason (with Fletcher Pratt), Ballantine Books (forthcoming in 1970). A tour of the magical kingdom of Oberon and Titania, but not quite as Shakespeare pictured it in *A Midsummer Night's Dream*. In The Ballantine Fantasy Series, for the first time in paperback.

ACK VANCE:

The Dying Earth, Lancer Books, 1969. Reissue of a modern fantasy classic first published in 1950. A little miracle of sparkling, witty, super-imaginative writing.

The Eyes of the Overworld, Ace Books, 1966. The fantasy

novel written as sequel to the above. Somewhat less bril
liant, but still a pleasure to read. Vance is one of the mos
delightful of living fantasy writers.

C. S. LEWIS:

Perelandra, Collier Books, 1962. A volume in the Ranson
trilogy, fascinating theological fantasy set on the plane
Venus. You will want to read the entire trilogy.

Prince Caspian, Penguin Books, 1965. Perhaps the best o
the seven Narnia books. A little like E. Nesbit but mor
adventurous. Most highly recommended.

The Great Divorce, Macmillan Paperbacks, 1963. An ex
traordinary adult fantasy novel laid in Heaven—but no
quite the Heaven you heard about in Sunday school!

J. R. R. TOLKIEN:

The Tolkien Reader, Ballantine Books, 1966. You will o
course have already read *The Lord of the Rings* (and i
you haven't—pay no attention to anything on this list, bu
run out and get it); the present collection contains on
play, two fairy-tales and a collection of Bombadil poems
Charming.

Smith of Wootton Major & Farmer Giles of Ham, Ballan
tine Books, 1969. Two tales. The second of them, "Farme
Giles," is one of the most perfect and delicious fairy-tale
of the 20th Century.

LIN CARTER:

Thongor in the City of Magicians, Paperback Library
1968. A Sword & Sorcery novel of heroic adventure an
evil sorcery in ancient Lemuria, the lost continent in th
Pacific.

Giant of World's End, Belmont Books, 1969. An attemp
at creating an heroic myth. Laid in the future supercont
nent of Gondwane *circa* seven hundred million A.D. M
own favorite of my novels.

The Black Star, Dell Books (forthcoming in 1970). Th
first volume in my new Atlantis trilogy.